Early Literacy

for Young Catholics

Pre-Kindergarten Activity Book

by Nan Alcott
Illustrated by Ben Hatke

Seton Press
Front Royal, Virginia

Printed in the United States of America

Seton Home Study School
1350 Progress Drive
Front Royal, VA 22630

(540) 636-9990 phone
(540) 636-1602 fax

Internet: www.setonhome.org
E-mail: info@setonhome.org

ISBN: 978-1-60704-094-1

Dedicated to the Blessed Mother

TABLE OF CONTENTS

WELCOME

to

SETON HOME STUDY SCHOOL'S PRE-KINDERGARTEN PROGRAM!

May you refresh your own wonder and curiosity as you work and play with your young child. Not only will this be a year to reflect and teach each of the topics in the eight units, it will be a time to introduce concepts and to expose your child to vocabulary, the notion of letters and sounds, many sensory activities as precursors to handwriting, as well as print and book awareness in a developmentally appropriate way for a four year old.

Two key points:

- This book is activity based because preschoolers learn best by doing and playing.
- This book is a year of exposure, not mastery, of the alphabet or sounds.

Our goal is to help parents create a Catholic and child-friendly learning environment, as well as to provide guidance and materials with which to teach.

Preparing a Catholic home environment

Our Faith is precious, and our traditions are rich. Preschoolers do not understand the depths of the mysteries of our Faith; however, they absorb a tremendous amount by ardently observing what we as parents do. Even one-year-olds at the table will stop and watch intently as the family makes the Sign of the Cross and prays grace together. You will find simple, suggested activities throughout this book which are consciously designed to emphasize the Catholic faith in your home life.

Preparing a child-friendly home environment

As parents, you began building a child-friendly environment before your child was born. You made your home and car safe for an infant with a crib and a car seat. As he became more mobile, you may have added outlet covers, gates, and a highchair. As he learned to crawl and walk, padding the sharp corners, putting cleaning materials out of reach, and keeping the bathroom door closed became routine matters.

AN IMPORTANT NOTE

Why are the letters not introduced in ABC order?

The letters are not introduced in alphabetical order, but rather based on the ease of the strokes required to make them. The activity book itself begins with pages where your child can scribble, and can trace simple vertical, horizontal, and circular lines.

Preparing a learning friendly home environment

The task now is to make your home learning friendly. This means

1. arranging things so that whatever your child can do independently is easy for him to do;
2. having a designated space for toys and materials;
3. dedicating time daily and often to teach your child to put materials away before each transition;
4. storing extra materials out of reach on a shelf, in a box or storage bin;
5. rotating activities according to parent decisions and ability to supervise.

Some ideas you may wish to borrow for a good preschool classroom

In a good preschool classroom, you would see the following:

- A designated space for belongings.
- Child-sized chair and table so the child's feet touch the floor.
- Specific areas for play with items separated and stored on low shelves.

Homes are not the same as classrooms

Of course, this is a description of a preschool classroom. Homes are very different than classrooms. We live in our homes 24 hours a day, all week, with our whole family. There is no custodian who cleans the bathrooms and vacuums. There is usually no extra time without students to prepare for the next day. Many activities will take place at the kitchen table, or on the living room floor. However, what follows is a basic principle which will work for your home.

Important principle for homes and classrooms

It is easier to keep track of fewer items.

Parents can control the available choices. Items do not have to be available all the time. Shelves, boxes, or storage bins for extra materials and toys are helpful. That being said, the following are invaluable for preschoolers to experiment and play with when you as the parent want to make them available.

Essential learning materials for the preschool child

- Playdough (homemade recipe is in book)
- Water (bath time, sink, dishpan, wading pool)
- Sensory materials
- Blocks (wooden, plastic, or make your own with taped up cardboard boxes)
- "Junk" to make things (paper towel tubes, items from your recycle bin, masking tape)
- Vertical surface on which to draw or paint (chalkboard, dry erase board, easel, paper taped to a big cardboard box or to the wall)
- Art supplies (paper, crayons, scissors, tape, glue, trash can)
- Puzzles, lacing cards, large beads or spools to string on a shoe lace.
- Books, magazines, printed materials, signs.
- Paper made into little notepads, (for shopping lists, playing restaurant) and pencils.

These materials help a preschool-aged child by enabling him to visualize connections, to experience and talk about concepts, to increase motor control, and to develop the hand-eye coordination necessary for future handwriting.

Coloring is an important technique to further develop fine-motor skills. Religious art for your child to color and display is included in the Appendix.

One last point!

Preschoolers need time outside everyday! To enjoy God's creation and the weather, to run, climb and move, to dig and jump with no fear of knocking over fragile items!

Our hope is that this book will assist you in teaching your preschool child Catholic values and culture, along with essential pre-literacy skills. May God bless your family in this endeavor!

Skills

The Virginia Department of Education has published *Virginia's Foundation Blocks for Early Learning: Comprehensive Standards for Four-Year-Olds (2013).* In this publication which can be accessed online, essential skills for four year olds are outlined in the areas of Literacy, Mathematics, Science, History and Social Science, Physical and Motor Development, and Personal and Social Development.

In this book, the emphasis is in the area of Literacy. Four of the six Literacy Foundation Blocks are addressed: Vocabulary, Phonetic Awareness, Letter Knowledge and Written Expression. The other two components, Oral Expression, and Print and Book Awareness, are covered in the accompanying lesson plans, which may be ordered through Seton Home Study School.

Bible References

The Bible references in the Activity Book are translations appropriate for understanding by the preschool child.

About the Author

Nan Alcott holds her Master of Education in Early Childhood Special Education from James Madison University. Her Bachelor of Arts in Elementary Education/Special Education is from Marygrove College.

Early Literacy for Young Catholics draws extensively on her experience of 21 years as a Special Education teacher, nine of which have beeen at the preschool level.

Nan has taught Catechesis of the Good Shepherd for seven years and homeschooled her youngest child for three high school years. Of her sterling achievements, Nan is perhaps most proud to state that she is "blessed to be a wife, mother of 6, and grandmother of 12."

About the Illustrator

Ben Hatke is an artist, writer, and comics creator. His work for Seton Press includes *Vocabulary for Young Catholics* and the upcoming Seton Edition of *Ballad of the White Horse.*

Ben learned painting by studying the Italian Masters and by training at the Charles Cecil Studios in Florence, Italy.

He lives and works in Front Royal, Virginia, with his lovely wife and growing family. Ben enjoys swords and whistles and juggling and adventures.

GOD MADE THE WONDERS OF CREATION

WHAT YOU WILL FIND IN UNIT 1

- The Letters T, O, and E
- The Sounds /t/, /o/, and /e/
- The Tripod Grasp
- Heavenly Writing
- Matching
- Snipping with Scissors
- Yellow, Green, and Blue
- Following One Step Directions
- Vertical, Horizontal, and Circular lines
- Spoken Word to Print Correspondence

GOD MADE THE WONDERS OF CREATION

Take a walk outdoors. Then take a photo of something wonderful God has created and paste the photo here. Or, cut out a magazine picture of something beautiful God has created.

TRY THIS:

Talk about the photo together. Have your child watch you as you write the words telling what it is.

LORD, HELP ME TODAY TO SEE THE WONDERS OF YOUR CREATION THROUGH THE EYES OF MY CHILD, AND TO TAKE A FRESH LOOK AT THE BEAUTY YOU HAVE PROVIDED FOR US TO ENJOY.

GOD MADE THE EARTH, THE WATER, AND THE SUN

Color the land and water with big strokes. Help your child use a tripod hand grasp to trace and color the sun with yellow.

THE TRIPOD GRASP:

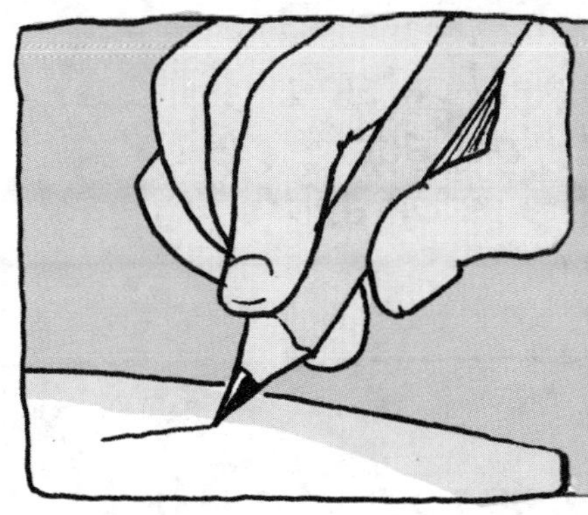

A tripod grasp is the correct way to hold a pencil or crayon for the smoothest use.

The pencil is held between the thumb and pointer finger, while resting on the middle finger. The ring and pinky fingers are tucked under.

GOD MADE THE MOON, THE STARS, AND THE SKY

Help your child use a tripod grasp to trace and color the moon with a yellow crayon. Color the stars with little scribbles.

TRY THIS:

Take your child outside on a clear night and point out the moon and stars to him.

GOD MADE TWO GREAT LIGHTS, THE GREATER ONE TO RULE THE DAY, AND THE LESSER ONE TO RULE THE NIGHT, AND THE STARS. GENESIS 1:16

HELLO, YELLOW!

Color with yellow.

TRY THIS:

Let your child help make scrambled eggs. Notice the yellow yolk. Have your child help you to stir it, and watch as you cook it.

THE TREES OF THE LORD DRINK THEIR FILL, THE CEDARS OF LEBANON, WHICH YOU PLANTED. PSALM 103:16

I SEE GREEN

Color with green.

TRY THIS:

Let your child help you to tear up lettuce for a salad this week. Tearing paper (or lettuce) helps preschoolers develop the small muscles of the hand, which they will need for handwriting.

HEAVENLY WRITING

1. Stand next to your child.

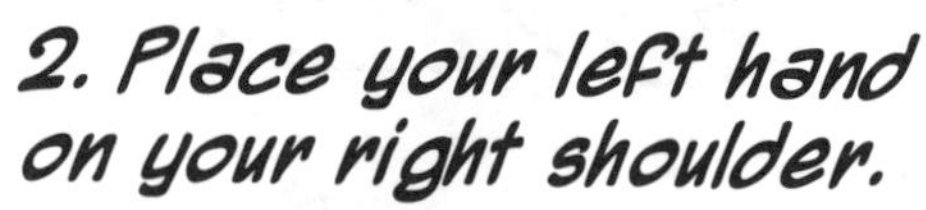
2. Place your left hand on your right shoulder.

3. Draw a big letter in the air. Use your whole right arm.

4. Child copies three times.

Note: If your child is left-handed, have her place her right hand on her left shoulder, and move her left arm to write the letter.

A TIME FOR TURTLES

Color the picture.

TURTLE

Look at the stroke sequence for the letter T. Before your child attempts this page, he should practice making Ts in the air with Heavenly Writing.

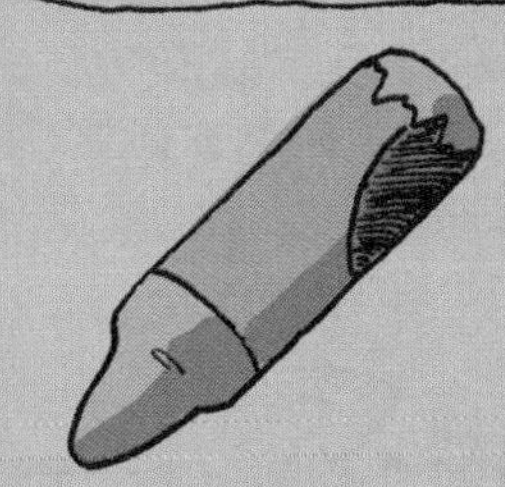

Giving small (3" or less) pieces of crayon or chalk to use will encourage the three fingers to use the tripod grasp.

T I CAN SAY "T"

Circle the Ts and color the tiger.

Refer to the pronunciation guide in the FAQ in the back of the workbook. Introduce the sound by saying it clearly, and close to your child, so he can see your mouth. "This letter says /t/." Emphasize that tiger, turtle, and tuba all start with the /t/ sound.

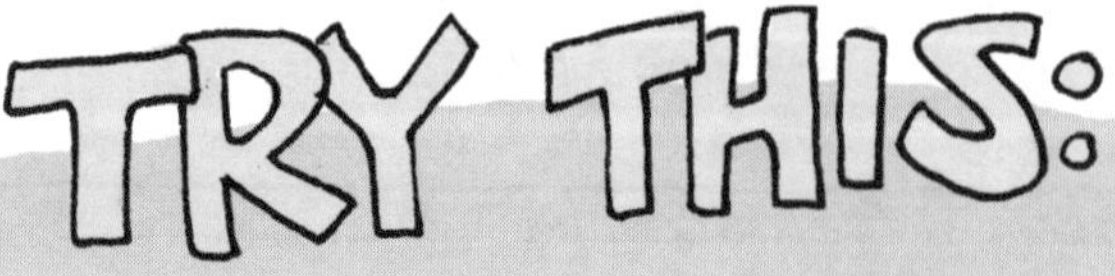

Purchase a clear, plastic over-the-door shoe holder with 24 pockets. Print one upper case letter on each pocket with a permanent marker. Pair W and X, Y and Z. With your child, collect items which begin with each sound as it is introduced and place in the pocket.

THERE'S a TIGER IN MY TUB!
Name all the things that start with /t/. Color the picture.
MY ALPHABET BOOK
During the year, in a 3 ring binder, start a sheet for each new letter. Your child may trace the letter. Have her glue pictures of items which begin with that letter to put on the opposite page. Remember to print the word under the picture as she watches.
Tip: This is a great place to reinforce Catholic imagery. Start with T-Tabernacle.
A
A A A
A A A

A TIGER AND A TURTLE TOO!

Circle all the Ts and color the turtle.

A Rebus Story uses pictures to tell a story. Help your child "read" the rebus pictures as you read the sentences and point with your finger, left to right. Listen for the /t/ words.

BLUE TOO!

Color with blue.

Playing with Legos, Tinker Toys, or other small manipulative toys will help develop the muscles to use a tripod grasp.

YOU MAKE a NEW COLOR

YELLOW ______ BLUE

Set out three glasses. Place 1/2 cup of water into each of 2 glasses. Let your child help to put 1 drop of yellow food coloring into the first glass, and 1 drop of blue food coloring into the third glass. Have him color the water in the glasses on the page to match.

Then, have your child pour some of each into the middle glass. See what it makes! Parent writes the color it makes on the line above, and child colors in the middle glass with the correct color.

I MET a TIGER TODAY.

Say the names of the pictures with your child. Circle the pictures that begin with /t/.

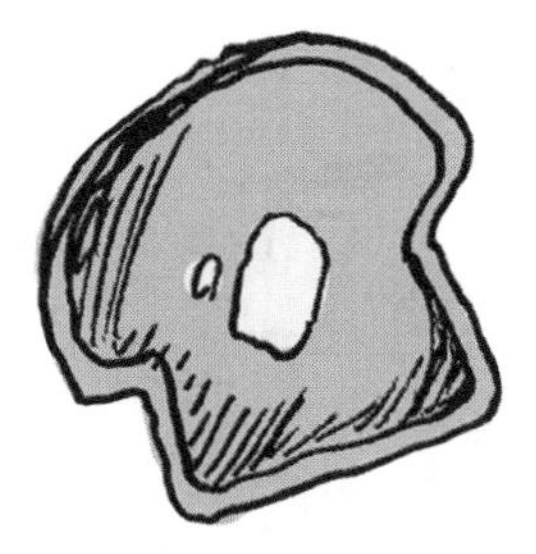

FEED the TIGER!

Glue or tape the Tiger face from the Appendix on a cracker box or small cereal box. Cut the box partially so that you can "open" the tiger's mouth. Have your child feed the tiger with items that start with /t/. Children love to hear the Tiger "roar" when they are successful.

The pictures are chicks, turtle, fish, tulip, toast.

IS IT BLUE, YELLOW OR GREEN?

Color with blue, yellow, green.

TRY THIS: Look for the color chasuble (vestment) the priest wears at Mass this Sunday. Find the blue of Mary's robes in a statue at home or in church. Light a candle on your home altar or at night prayers and talk about the yellow candle flames.

GOD MADE THE FLOWERS AND THE PLANTS

Use a tripod grasp to trace stems. Finger print or dip eraser end of the pencil in a bit of green finger paint and "stamp" on the leaves.

. . . SEE, I GIVE YOU EVERY SEED-BEARING PLANT ON ALL THE EARTH. . .
GENESIS 1:29

Look at the stroke sequence for the letter O. Before your child attempts this page, he should practice making Os in the air using Heavenly Writing.

OWL, OTTER AND OCTOPUS, OH, MY!

Circle the Os and color the Pictures

OWL

OTTER

OCTOPUS

Introduce the sound by saying it clearly and close to your child, so he can see your mouth. "This letter says /o/." Emphasize that owl, otter, and octopus all start with the /o/ sound.

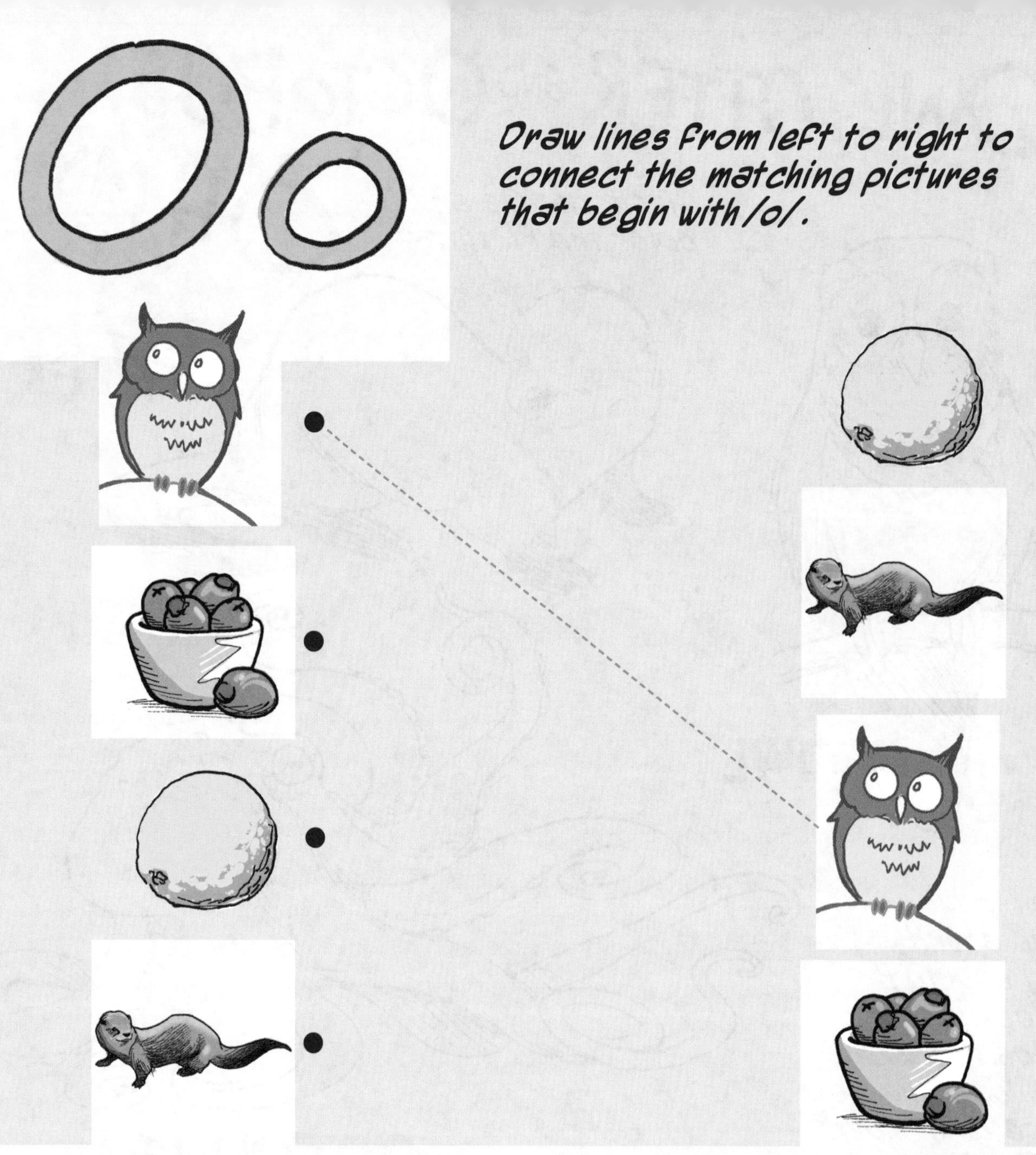

Draw lines from left to right to connect the matching pictures that begin with /o/.

TRY THIS:

Send your child on a mission to find things that begin with O.

You or he can print O on "sticky notes." His mission is to find items, put the "sticky notes" on them, and report back to you.

The pictures are owl, olives, orange, otter.

YELLOW, GREEN, and BLUE

I CAN SEE THEM ... CAN YOU?

Parent: Cut out the blue, yellow, and green strips, and the images from the appendix on page 227.

Have your child snip small squares and ornaments from the strips and help him glue the pieces onto the stained glass window in any design.

TRY THIS:

If your church has stained glass windows, name the colors in them.

E

Look at the stroke sequence for the letter E. Before your child attempts this page, he should practice making Es with Heavenly Writing.

Circle the Es and color the elf's hat.

Ee

Introduce the sound by saying it clearly, and close to your child, so he or she can see your mouth. "This letter says /eh/." Emphasize that egg, elephant, and envelope all start with the /eh/ sound.

CHILDREN LEARN THROUGH MANY SENSES.

Let your child experiment with writing in salt on a cookie sheet. When teaching a specific letter, always demonstrate the correct stroke for your child first.

TIP: Save the used salt in a small plastic container with a lid to be used another time.

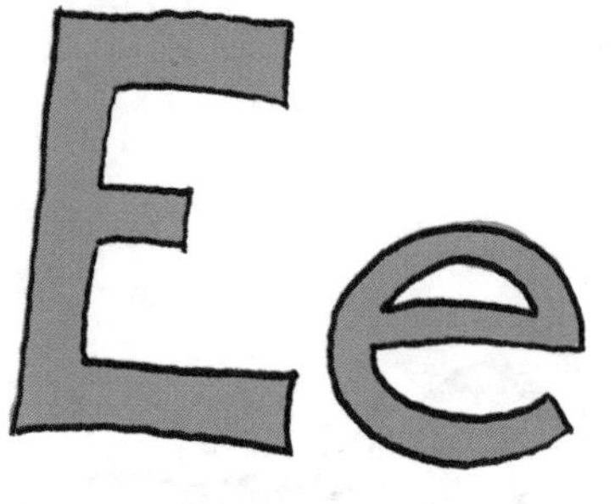

Draw lines from left to right to connect the matching pictures that begin with /e/.

SIDEWALK LETTERS

Have your child make big letters on a horizontal surface. Try sidewalk chalk; fingers in a sandbox or on a beach; a stick in smooth dirt or light snow.

The pictures are elephant, elf, envelope, Eskimo, eggplant.

GOD MADE BEAUTIFUL THINGS FOR ME TO SEE

Let your child choose pictures to glue in the frames. Parent writes word under each picture. Use this as a picture litany to pray: "Thank you, God, for. . ."

MAY THE GLORY OF THE LORD ENDURE FOREVER;
MAY THE LORD BE GLAD IN HIS WORKS!" PSALM 104:31

SAME and DIFFERENT

Draw a line to connect the pictures to their shadows.

TRY THIS:

On a sunny day, have your child place items (plastic fork, pencil, scissors) outside on blue construction paper. Leave in the sun for two hours. As the sun fades the paper, a "shadow" of the object appears.

The pictures are eagle, duck, frog, fish, turtle.

GOD MADE THE ANIMALS

WHAT'S NEW IN UNIT 2

- The Letters L, F, and B
- The Sounds /l/, /f/, and /b/
- Classifying and Similarities
- Tracing Diagonal Lines
- Concepts: Big/Small
- Brown, Orange, Red, and Black
- Directionality: Reading Left to Right on a Page
- Listening for Words that Begin with the Same Sound

GOD MADE THE ANIMALS

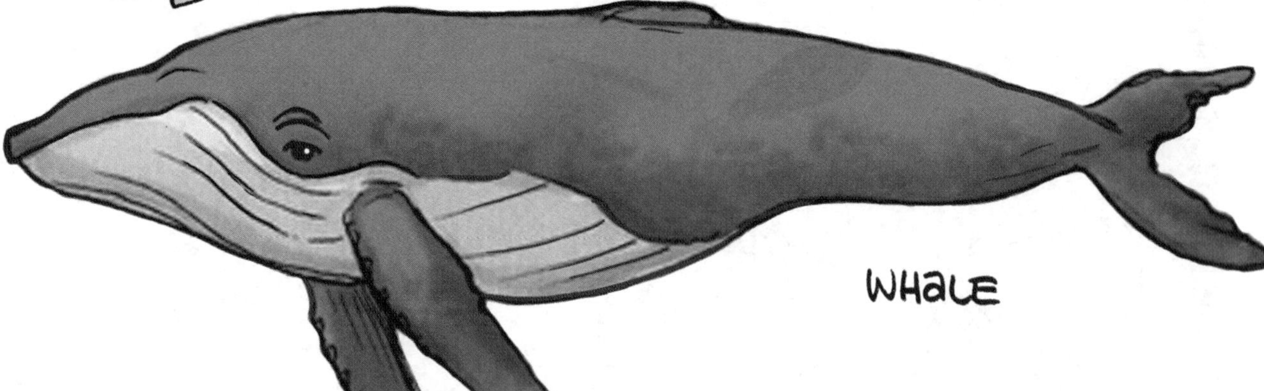

Color the mouse.

MY FRIEND THE TOUCAN:

Let your child draw or glue pictures of animals on a page. Have your child watch while you write the name of the animal.

DEAR GOD, THANK YOU FOR CREATING ALL THE WONDERFUL ANIMALS, BIG AND SMALL.

WHERE THE ANIMALS LIVE

Find these pictures in the appendix on page 227. Cut them out and glue them on the page.

IS THAT A TURTLE IN THE TREE?

Talk about the habitats of the animals on the page. Why does the bird live in the tree?

Why does the turtle have a shell? Why does the rabbit hop so fast?

BROWN ALL AROUND

Color with brown.

TRY THIS:

Look around your home for things that are colored brown. Make chocolate pudding or share toast with peanut butter and honey. As you eat, talk about other things colored brown.

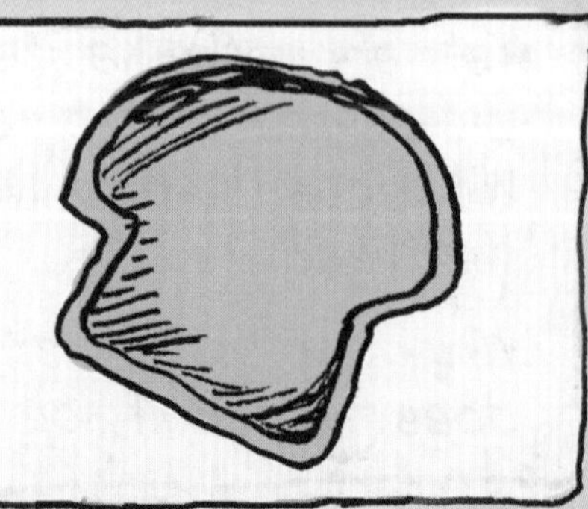

Help your child use a tripod grasp to trace the grass. Color the lion's mane.

YOUNG LIONS ROAR FOR PREY;
THEY SEEK THEIR FOOD FROM GOD. PSALM 104:21

A LITTLE LION

Circle the Ls.

FINGER EXERCISES:

Rolling play dough into long rolls strengthens fingers. Show your child how to form letters, using the correct stroke sequence.

Learning the shape of a letter is difficult, and often hard to duplicate with a pencil.

Practice Heavenly Writing and then trace the Ls.

DO LAMBS LIKE LADDERS?

"This letter says /l/." Say the /l/ words, letting your child repeat them.

Color the picture.

ON THE LETTER HUNT:

Go on an /l/ hunt around the home or outside. Help your child find things that begin with the sound of /l/: lamp, leaf, lid. Use sticky notes with the letter L printed on them. Add L items to your letter pocket.

Draw lines from left to right to connect the matching pictures that begin with /l/.

FEED the LION

Glue or tape the lion face from the Appendix on a cracker box or small cereal box. Cut the box partially so that you can "open" the tigers mouth. Have your child feed the Lion with L pictures in the appendix.

Note: Include two or three other letter (distractor) cards.

The pictures are lego, leaves, ladle, lemur, and list.

CAN YOU FIND THEIR MOTHER?

Draw a line from the mother animals to their babies.

LET'S SING ALONG

To the tune of "The Wheels on the Bus"

One little bird said tweet, tweet, tweet,
tweet, tweet, tweet, tweet, tweet, tweet.
One little bird said tweet, tweet, tweet,
All over town.
Continue with other animals.

The pictures are bird, frog, cat, duck.

SAME and DIFFERENT

Say the name of the first picture in each row. Cross out the picture in each row that does not match the first picture.

The pictures are lion, lollipop, lemon, lunchbox, lamb.

BLACK as a CROW

Color the picture with black.

TRY THIS

Look around the house or neighborhood for items that are black.

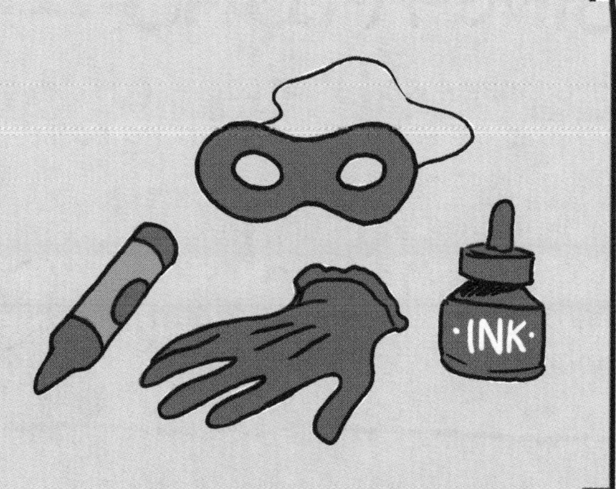

God Made Small Animals

Help your child use a tripod grasp to trace the horizontal lines. Color the pictures.

Sing-A-Long:

Five green and speckled frogs
Sitting on a hollow log eating some most delicious bugs. (Yum, yum!)

One jumped into the pool,
Where it was nice and cool,
Then there were four green
Speckled frogs. (Glub, glub)

THEN GOD SAID: LET THE WATER TEEM WITH AN ABUNDANCE OF LIVING CREATURES, AND ON THE EARTH LET BIRDS FLY BENEATH THE DOME OF THE SKY. GENESIS 1: 21

CLEVER as a FOX
Circle the Fs.
Color the picture.
FALSE FOX
FEZ
FIREFLY
FOX
FOLIAGE
HOME MADE PLAY DOUGH
1 cup salt
2 cups flour
4 tbsp. cream of tartar
A few drops food coloring
2 cups water
2 tablespoons oil
Mix all in a heavy saucepan, stir over medium heat. When all the liquid is gone, turn out onto plastic wrap. Cool a bit, and knead. Store covered, or in a zip-lock bag.
Practice Heavenly Writing and then trace the Fs.

"This letter says /f/." Say the /f/ words, letting your child repeat them.

Color the picture.

Place "lily pads" on the floor and jump from one to another. How many times before you land in the water?

SOUND OF F REBUS STORY

Help your child "read" the rebus pictures as you read the sentences and point with your finger, left to right. Listen for the /f/ words.

A  sat under the flowers.

They watched the fish float by.

Circle the Fs.
Color the pictures.

IF I WERE A FISH...

I would live in the ____________________,

I would play with ____________________,

and I would eat ____________________.

What else would I do?

GOD MADE SOME ANIMALS WITH STRIPES

Help your child use a tripod grasp to make stripes on the zebra. Can you think of other striped animals?

DO YOU HAVE STRIPES?

Go through your closet and see how many things have stripes! Find pictures of striped animals in animal books.

LET THEM ALL PRAISE THE LORD'S NAME; FOR HE COMMANDED AND THEY WERE CREATED, . . .PSALM 148:5

ALL OVER ORANGE

TRY THIS:

Look around your home for things that are colored orange. Help your mom make orange juice.

Draw lines from left to right to connect the matching pictures that begin with /f/.

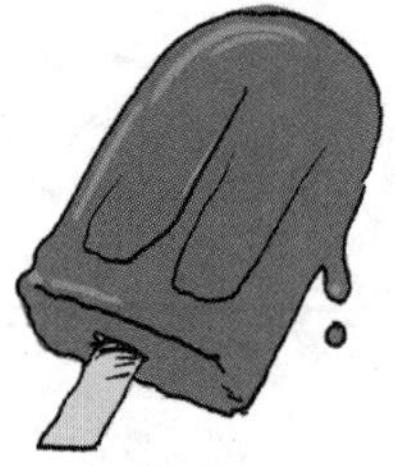

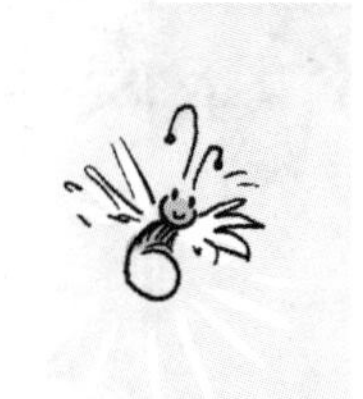

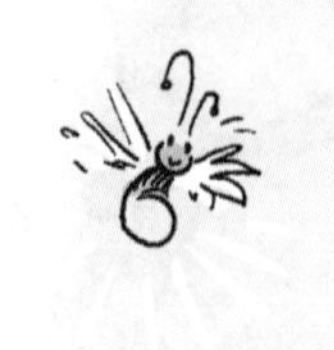

MAGNET FISHING

Parent: cut out pictures that begin with /f/ and attach a paper clip to each one. Include a few distractors. Make a pole with string and a magnet and fish for /f/ items. Can be used for other sounds too!

The pictures are frog, firefly, fox, fudgesicle, fish.

Help your child make spots on the animal either using his finger prints or using the eraser end of a pencil. Dip the finger or the eraser end of the pencil in a bit of black finger paint and "stamp" on the spots.

PRAISE THE LORD FROM THE EARTH. . .
ANIMALS WILD AND TAME. . . PSALM 148: 7, 10

GOD MADE SOME ANIMALS WITH SPIKES

RIDDLE THIS

How do porcupines play leap frog?
Very carefully!

SO THE LORD GOD FORMED OUT OF THE GROUND ALL THE WILD ANIMALS AND ALL THE BIRDS OF THE AIR. . . GENESIS 2:19

NED'S RED BED

Color with red.

MY OH MY, PIZZA PIE

Look around your home for things that are colored red, and make a pretend pizza.

GOD MADE SOME ANIMALS WITH WHISKERS

CAT

CATFISH

Trace whiskers and color.

MOUSE

HOLD THE WHISKERS!

Recipe for an "Open Face" sandwich: Pinch a piece of bread at the two top corners to make "ears." Then spread with PB& J. Here's looking at you! Add pretzels, or celery sticks for whiskers.

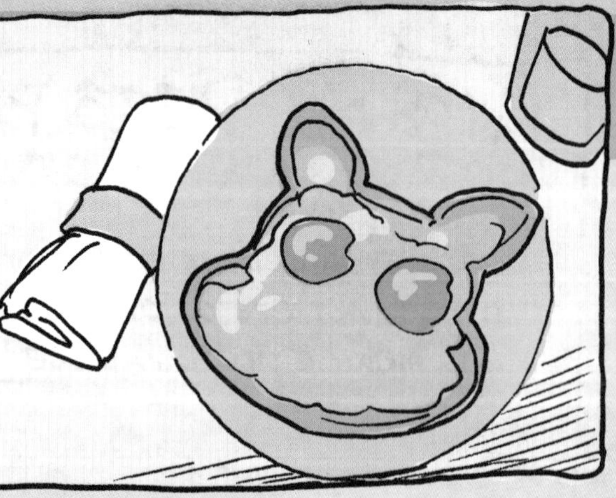

THEN GOD SAID: LET THE EARTH BRING FORTH EVERY KIND OF LIVING CREATURE: TAME ANIMALS, CRAWLING THINGS, AND EVERY KIND OF WILD ANIMAL... GENESIS 1:24

Practice Heavenly Writing and then trace the Bs.

GOD MADE SOME ANIMALS WITH FEATHERS

Color the sparrow. Use a pencil eraser dipped in finger paint to make dots for bird seed for the birds to eat. Can you think of other birds?

BIRDS ARE HUNGRY TOO!

Hang a pinecone birdfeeder made of peanut butter and birdseed from a tree and observe the different birds that come to eat.

GOD CREATED.....ALL KINDS OF WINGED BIRDS. GENESIS 1:21

Bb

Circle the Bs.

"This letter says /b/." Say the /b/ words, letting your child repeat them.

TRY THIS:

Visit a Pet Store.

See how many different birds live there. If you were one of the birds, what would you do all day?

Walk out to your yard and look for all the varieties around you.

Bb

Say the names of the pictures with your child. Circle the pictures that begin with /b/.

BEAR

B'S IN MY BED

After your child makes her bed, have her put 5 items that begin with the /b/ sound on the bed. Add some /b/ items to the letter pockets.

The pictures are bee, frog, ball, mouse, bird, dog.

GOD MADE ME SPECIAL

WHAT'S NEW IN UNIT 3

- The Letters H, I, C, and U
- The Sounds /h/, /i/, /c/, and /u/
- Recognition of Letters in Name
- Recognition of Own Name
- Tracing Name
- Measurement and Measuring Tools
- Rectangle, Square, Triangle, Circle
- Concepts of Long/Short, Heavy/Light
- Person: Three Dimensional to Two Dimensional

GOD MADE ME SPECIAL

Help your child to glue a photograph of himself on this page. Talk about how your child is special to you.

SING-A-LONG

To the tune of Yankee Doodle
Add your own hand motions.

God the Father loves me so,
I am always wan-ted.
He gave me fingers, ears and toes,
and a nose to sneeze with.
God the Father loves me so,
all my hairs are coun-ted.
I am special and unique,
to God this song is lif-ted!

LORD, YOU HAVE CREATED EACH OF US TO BE UNIQUE. HELP ME TO APPRECIATE AND LOVE THIS LITTLE CHILD YOU HAVE GIVEN TO ME.

Have your child look in a mirror at his hair, eye, and skin color. Have him color in details to match how he looks. Print your child's name on the ribbon and have him trace over it.

TRULY YOU HAVE FORMED MY INMOST BEING;
YOU KNIT ME IN MY MOTHER'S WOMB. PSALM 139:13

CREATE-A-ME

Many young four-year-olds do not have the skills yet for representational drawing. If you ask them to draw a person, it's hard to tell what it is!
Using items around the house, help your child construct a person with a head, body, two eyes, a nose, arms, two hands, legs and feet. Keep these in a basket or bag, to complete on their own once you have demonstrated it.
The idea is to get a head (circle) right next to the body (rectangle) and to place the arms coming out of the body at the shoulders. Later, you can demonstrate drawing a person on a chalkboard or paper using the same shapes of circle and rectangle.

SING·A·LONG

Try this song to Old McDonald

Old McDonald had a head,
E-I-E-I-O
And on his head he had two eyes,
E-I-E-I-O
With one nose here
And a big smile there
Here an ear, there an ear
And on the top a bit of hair
Old McDonald had a head,
E-I-E-I-O

Old McDonald had a body,
E-I-E-I-O
And on this body he had two arms,
E-I-E-I-O
With one hand here
And another hand there,
Here a leg, there a leg,
Here a foot, there a foot,
Old McDonald had a body,
E-I-E-I-O

THIS IS ME TODAY

Add simple details of clothing, hair, features to the picture.

WHAT IS YOUR FAVORITE...

Talk about what colors the ginger-bread character is wearing.
What color is your favorite?

YOUR HANDS HAVE FORMED ME AND FASHIONED ME... JOB 10: 8

Introduce the names of the shapes: circle, square, triangle, and rectangle. Color and name the shapes.

AS THE SPARROW FINDS A HOME AND THE SWALLOW A NEST
TO SETTLE HER YOUNG, MY HOME IS BY YOUR ALTARS, LORD OF HOSTS,
MY KING AND MY GOD! PSALM 84: 4

H
HIPPO IN A HAYSTACK?
IPPO HAS A HAPPY HAT!
Color the hen.
HANDY HEN HELPS.
TOOLS
NOODLE DOODLE
Make an H with dry spaghetti noodles.
How about T, E, F, and L?
What else can you use to make letters?
Add H to the Alphabet Book.
Practice Heavenly Writing and then trace the Hs.
1
2
3

Color the picture.

"This letter says /h/." Say the /h/ words, letting your child repeat them.

A TREASURE HUNT:

Send your child on a hunt to find items that begin with H. You or your child can print H on sticky notes to place on the objects such as hat, hanger, horn or hair brush. Remember to add items to your letter pockets.

Hh

Say the names of the pictures with your child. Circle the pictures that begin with /h/.

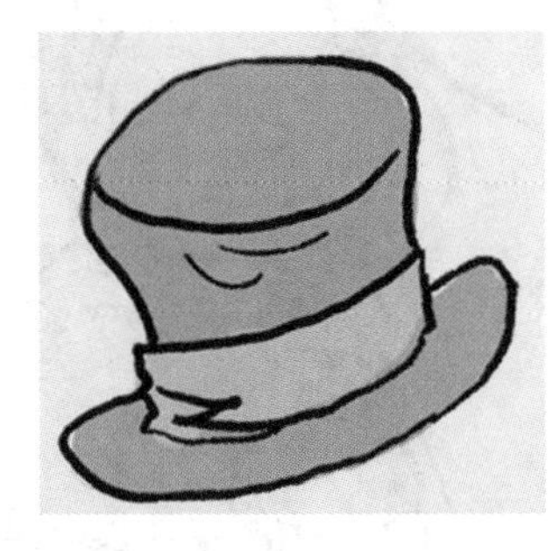

HUNGRY HAMSTER HUNT

Just for fun!

Make a pretend "Hamster" shopping list for your child to take on your next shopping trip. Help to find the items on the list.

The pictures are hat, hamburger, mask, heart, pumpkin.

I AM GROWING

DATE: ________________

I AM ______ YEARS OLD.

I WEIGH _____

I AM ____TALL.

Measure and weigh your child. Teach the names of what was used to measure: (scale and tape measure or yardstick). Have him watch as you record the numbers.

MEASURE UP!

Line up shoes to measure how long a rug is. Use straws to measure how long the couch is. What else can you use to measure?

I PRAISE YOU, BECAUSE I AM WONDERFULLY MADE ... PSALM 139: 14A

Practice Heavenly Writing and then trace the Is.

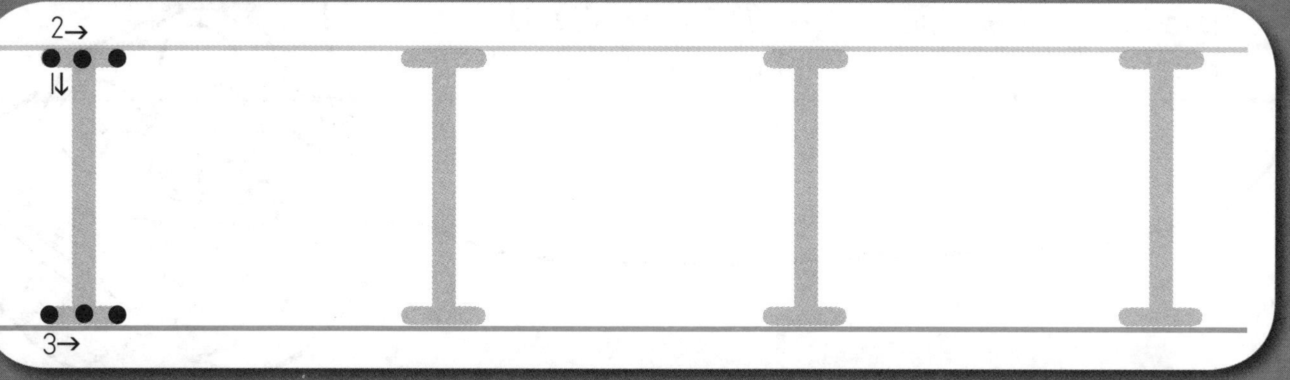

INSIDE THE IGLOO

"This letter says /i/." Say the /i/ words, letting your child repeat them.

SAME and DIFFERENT

Say the name of the first picture in each row. Cross out the picture in each row that does not match the first picture.

HOW MANY INCHWORMS?

The pictures are inchworm, insects, iguana, ice cream, ice.

MY NAME STARTS WITH THE LETTER...

A child's name is the most motivating word to begin to teach him, both to recognize and to print.

Parent, print the first letter of your child's name. Let your child trace the lines.

TRY THIS

Print the letter on cardboard or a large index card and trace it with tacky glue. Show how to glue dried beans on the letter outline.

DO NOT FEAR, FOR I HAVE REDEEMED YOU; I HAVE CALLED YOU BY NAME: YOU ARE MINE. ISAIAH 43:1B

THIS IS MY NAME

Following the alphabet model in the back of the workbook, print your child's first name with a highlighter. Have your child trace it with a pencil.

Best practice is for a child to trace over solid lines.

Writing is hard! Praise all efforts.

Another fun way to develop letter formation is covering a jelly roll pan or baking sheet with shaving cream, and let your child write in the foam.

SEE, UPON THE PALMS OF MY HANDS I HAVE ENGRAVED YOU;. . . ISAIAH 49: 16

Cc
CUPCAKES
COLOSSAL
CANDY
CANE
CAP
CLOWN
Color the clown and cupcakes.
CAR
CAT
BEND ME A LETTER
Shaping pipe cleaners is a good way for children to practice forming letters.
Practice Heavenly Writing and then trace the Cs.

Circle the Cs.
Color the camel.

"This letter says /c/." Say the /c/ words, letting your child repeat them.

Note that the hard "c" is the same sound as /k/.

At the grocery store or in your kitchen, find items that begin with /c/ like corn, cucumber, and carrots. Look for /c/ items for your letter pockets.

THE CAT AND THE CUCUMBER

Color the cucumber green and the corn yellow. Add flames to the candles.

Find all the Cs.

Help your child "read" the rebus pictures as you read the sentences and point with your finger, left to right. Listen for the /c/ words.

Say the name of the first picture in each row. Circle the picture in each row that matches the first picture.

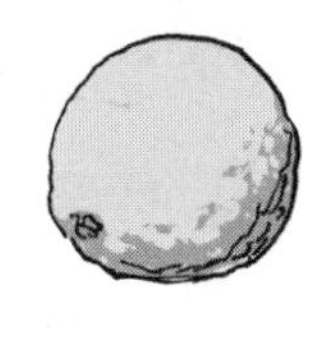

TRY THIS

Make /c/ things from Playdough.

The pictures are cats, cow, cake, clown, camel.

I HAVE ____ PEOPLE IN MY FAMILY.

On a sheet of paper, help your child to make a picture of your family. Using a washable stamp pad, child makes thumbprint for each face, and then draws stick figure. Add faces and hair.

Parent: label with names as child dictates. Count with your child, touching each figure. Parent writes number on line. Child may trace number.

A FATHER'S BLESSING GIVES A PERSON FIRM ROOTS, . . . SIRACH 3:9

CAN YOU MATCH THE SOCKS? CAN YOU NAME THE COLORS?

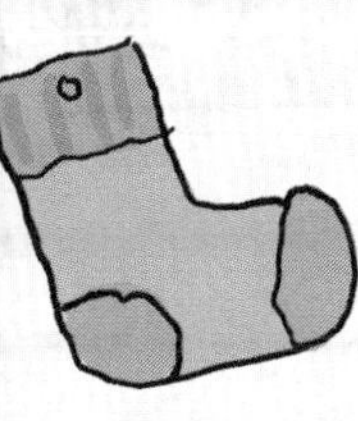

Let your child help you to match socks this week.

Practice counting them out loud.

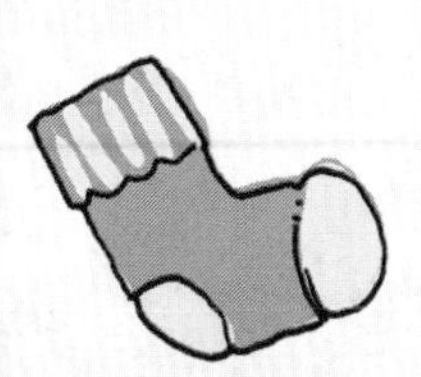

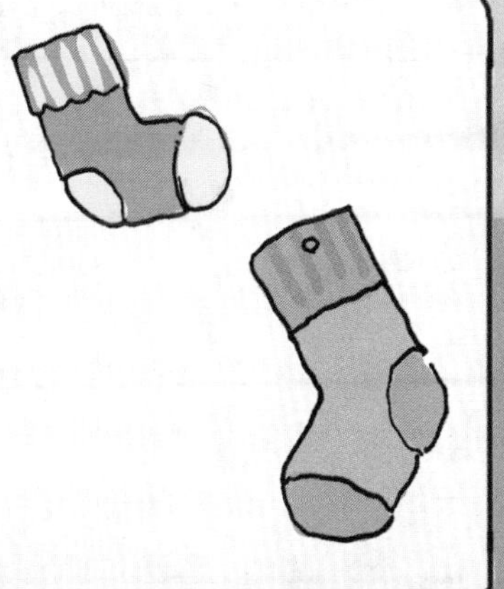

UNDER MY UMBRELLA
Color the pictures.
(UKULELE)
Practice Heavenly Writing and then trace the Us.
HIGH WATER, LOW WATER
Use a jump rope. Slowly raise the rope each time your child jumps over it. When it's too high, she can crawl under it.

UP, UNDER, OR UNTIED?

"This letter says /u/". Say the /u/ words, letting your child repeat them.

Color the balloon.

Add U to your alphabet book.

UP, DOWN, AND ALL AROUND

Look for three things that are up and three things that are under.

Draw lines from left to right to connect the matching pictures that begin with /u/.

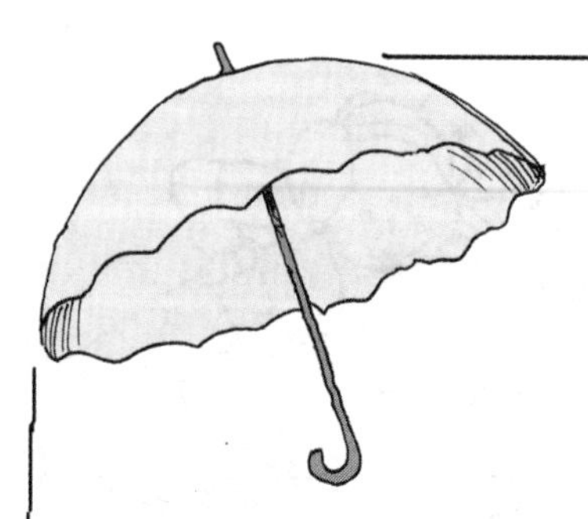

UNDER THE UMBRELLA GAME

Children love umbrellas. Take a walk in the rain under your dry umbrella. If it's sunny, set up a large umbrella and have a make believe "beach day." Don't forget the boogie boards and the sun screen!

The pictures are up, umbrella, under, ukulele, untied.

LONG AND SHORT

Circle the items that are longer.

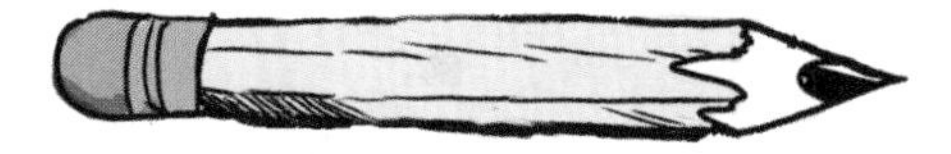

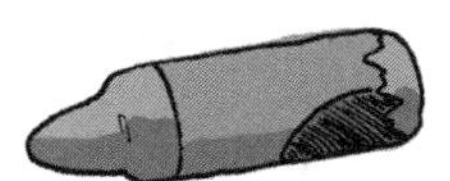

WHICH IS LONGER?

Compare objects of different lengths. Ask which is longer and shorter.

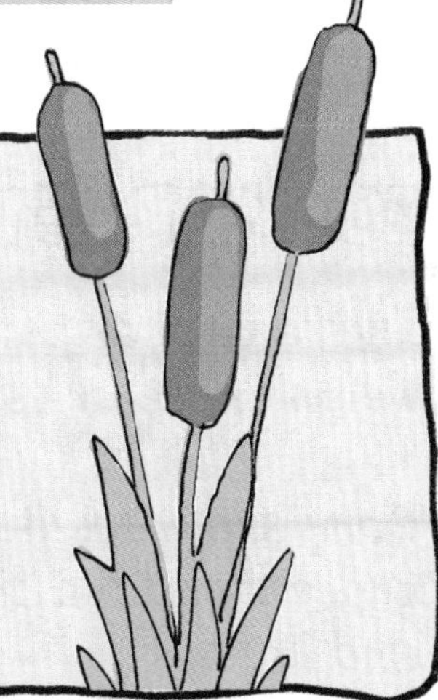

The pictures are pencil, paintbrush, crayon, beak, tail.

HEAVY AND LIGHT

Circle the items that are heavy. Underline the items that are light.

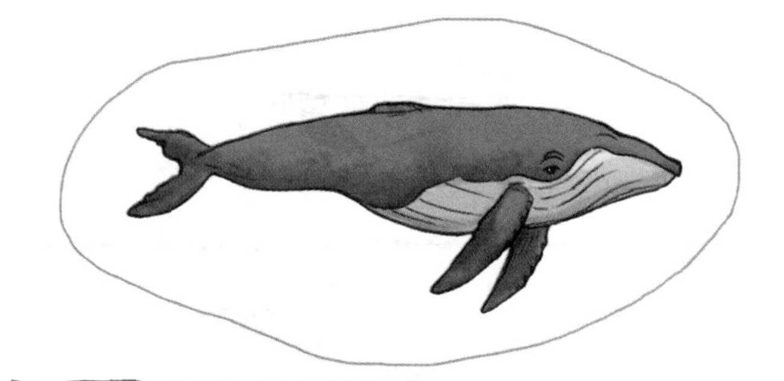

TO MARKET, TO MARKET

In the grocery store, let your child help weigh fruits or vegetables.

Compare many items to help your child understand the concepts of heavy and light.

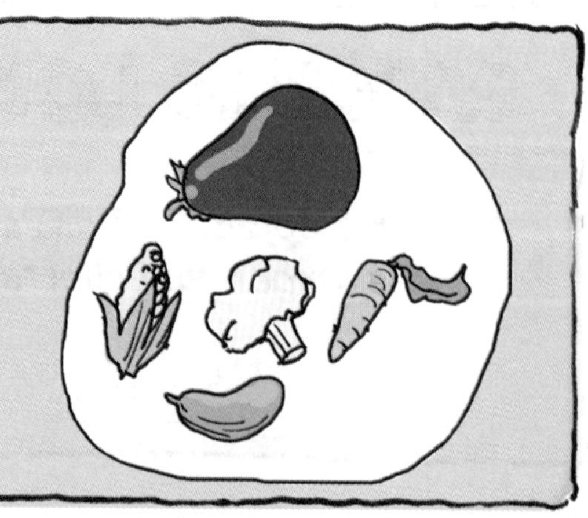

GOD MADE ALL THINGS, VISIBLE AND INVISIBLE

WHAT'S NEW IN UNIT 4

- The Letters A, M, and V
- The Sounds /a/, /m/, and /v/
- Clapping to Multi-Syllable Words
- Rhyming "Mat"
- Color Matching
- Purple and Pink

GOD MADE ALL THINGS, VISIBLE AND INVISIBLE

Draw a line between the matching angels.

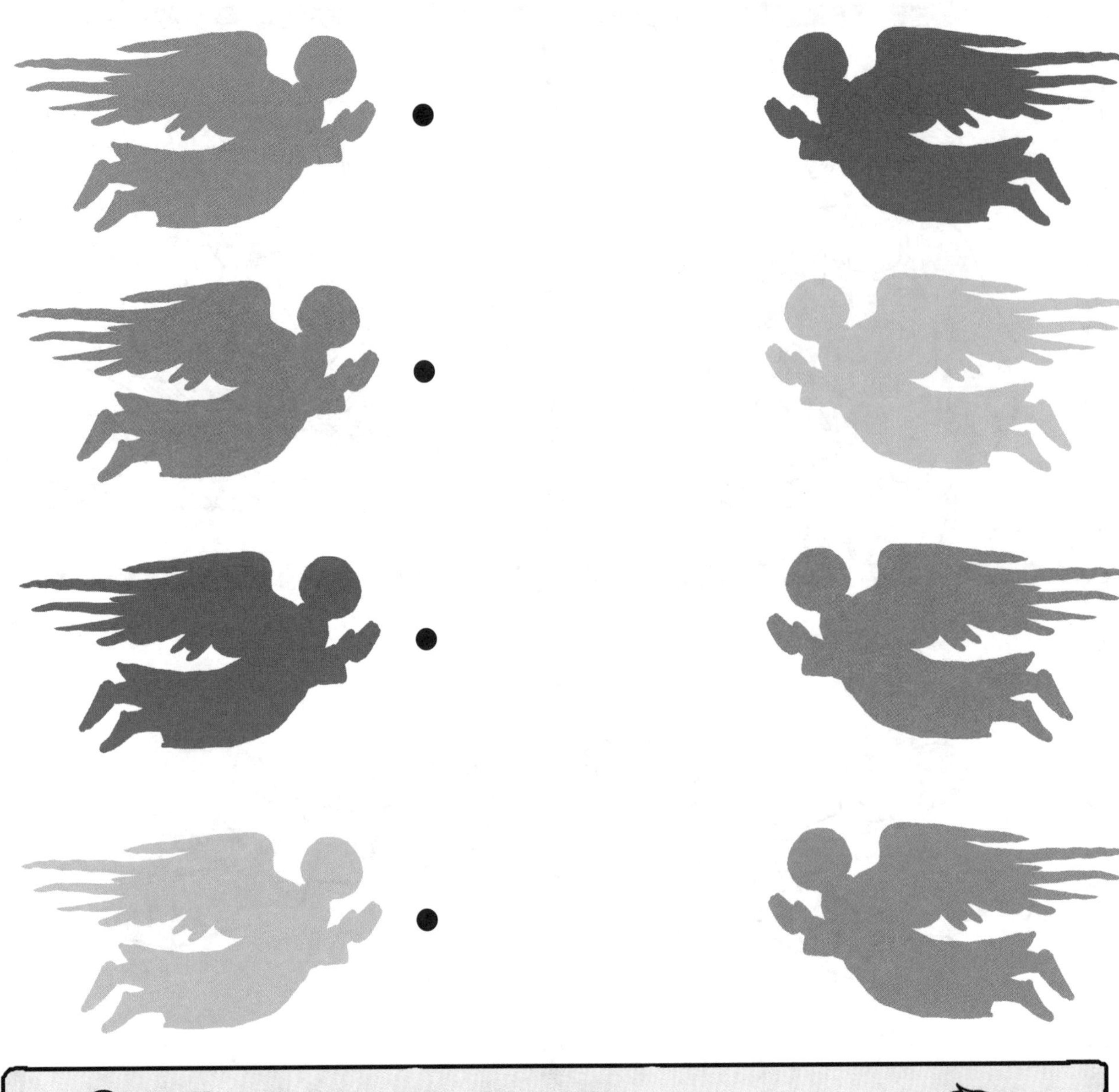

ONCE UPON AN ANGEL...

Try reading wonderful angel stories to your child. In a Bible story book, see the Book of Tobit (Tobias), Gospel of St. Luke - Angel Gabriel to Mary, Angels at the Birth of Jesus, and so on.

LORD GOD, YOU HAVE CREATED ALL THAT IS.
ALL THAT WE CAN SEE AND ALL THAT WE CANNOT SEE.
HELP ME TO TEACH MY CHILD ABOUT THE ANGELS,
WHO ALWAYS SEE AND PRAISE YOU.

Practice Heavenly Writing and then trace the As.

GOD MADE THE ANGELS

Color and count the angels.

ANGEL CRAFT

Make an angel using cardboard. Cut a circle and form a cone. Decorate with wings and make the head with something like a styrofoam ball or a stuffed baby sock.

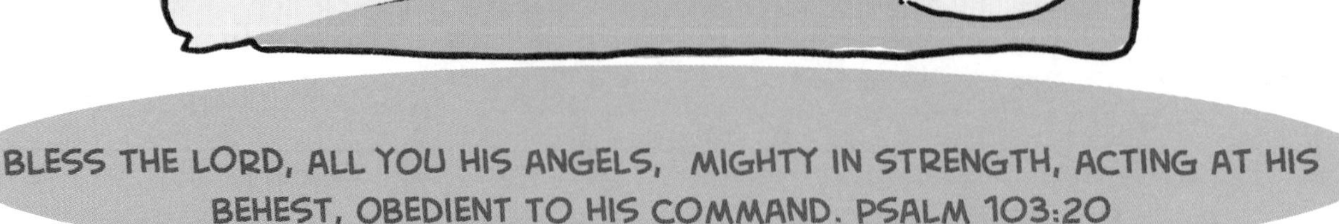

BLESS THE LORD, ALL YOU HIS ANGELS, MIGHTY IN STRENGTH, ACTING AT HIS BEHEST, OBEDIENT TO HIS COMMAND. PSALM 103:20

Color the Angelfish.

"This letter says /a/." Say the /a/ words, letting your child repeat them.

Sometimes A says its name, as in Angelfish.

Using cardboard, help your child draw and cut out an angelfish. Tape a stick on the back and...Go Swimming!

I Have a Guardian Angel

Use fingerprints or a pencil's eraser end to paint the angels' wings.

A Prayer for Your Guardian Angel

Clap to the syllables in guard-i-an an-gels.

Sing: All day, all night, angels watching over me, my Lord.
All day, all night, angels watching over me.

SEE THAT YOU DO NOT DESPISE ONE OF THESE LITTLE ONES,
FOR I SAY TO YOU THAT THEIR ANGELS IN HEAVEN ALWAYS LOOK UPON THE FACE OF MY HEAVENLY FATHER. MATTHEW 18:10

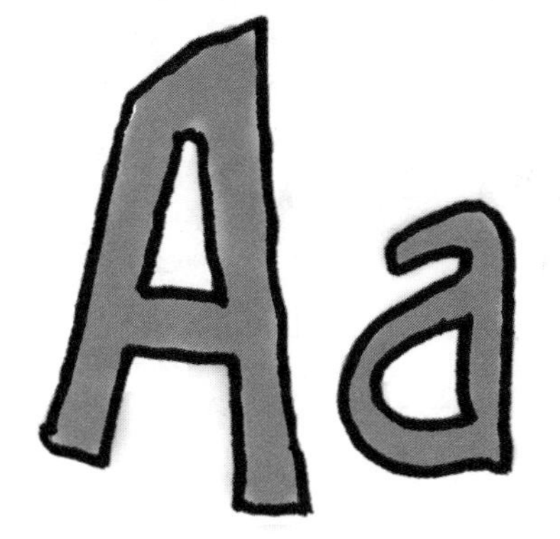

Say the names of the pictures with your child. Circle the pictures that begin with /a/.

ANGELFISH

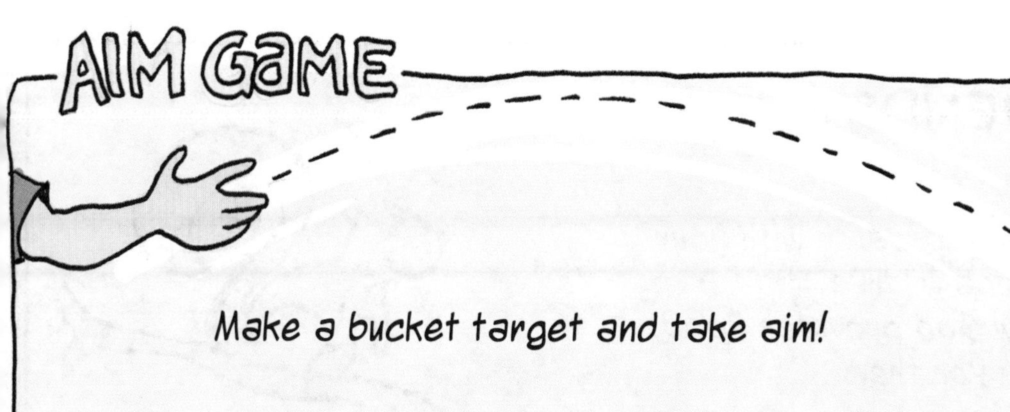

Make a bucket target and take aim!

The pictures are balloon, acorn, mug, angel and apron.

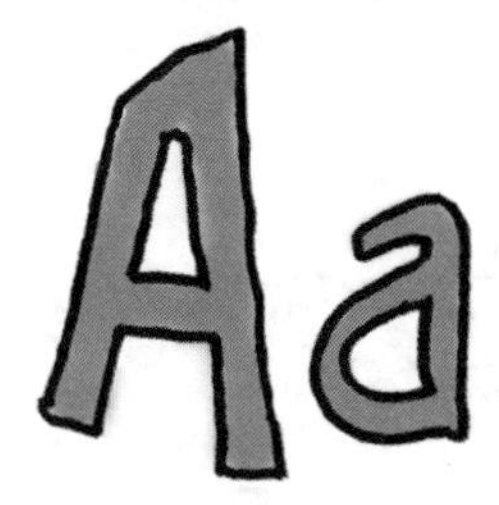

WHERE'S MY ACORN?

Color the squirrel.
Find the As.

April put an  in her 

A  took the  and ate it.

Help your child "read" the rebus pictures as you read the sentences and point with your finger, left to right. Listen for the /a/ words.

FURRY FRIENDS

Take a walk and watch with your child for area wildlife.
Discuss how God provides food and shelter for them.

I CAN'T SEE MY ANGEL,

BUT SOME PEOPLE HAVE SEEN ANGELS

Color the grapes purple.

. . . THE ANGEL GABRIEL WAS SENT FROM GOD . . .
TO A VIRGIN BETROTHED TO A MAN NAMED JOSEPH, . . . AND THE VIRGIN'S NAME WAS MARY. LUKE 1: 26,27

How many sheep? ___________

How many angels? ___________

How many shepherds? ___________

Color the stars yellow.

NOW THERE WERE SHEPHERDS IN THAT REGION LIVING IN THE FIELDS AND KEEPING THE NIGHT WATCH OVER THEIR FLOCK. THE ANGEL OF THE LORD APPEARED TO THEM AND THE GLORY OF THE LORD SHONE AROUND THEM,... LUKE 2: 8,9

PURPLE as a PLUM

Color the picture.

ALL THINGS PURPLE

Look for purple fruits and vegetables in the grocery store. Notice what color Chasuble (vestment) the priest wears during Advent. Help to make an Advent wreath.

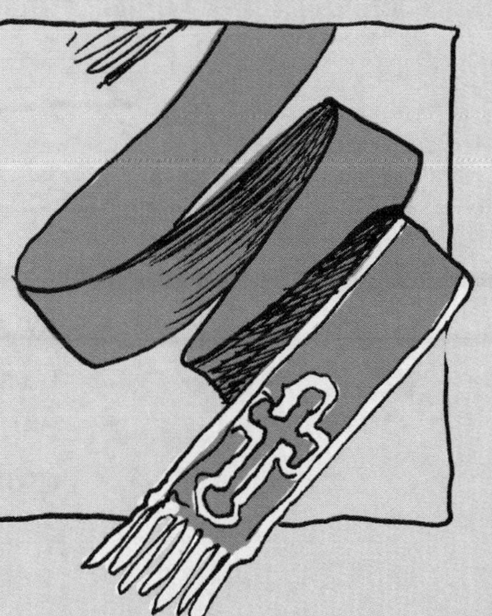

IN JACK HORNER'S CORNER
Training the ear to "hear" rhymes is the first step in learning to rhyme. So, get out the Mother Goose books and enjoy the age-old rhymes with your child!
When reading nursery rhymes, say the second rhyming word quietly, and encourage your child to say it too.
PLUM
THUMB
sniff sniff
Color the puppy.
RHYME A GOOD BOOK LATELY?
Read a rhyming book, LISTEN for the words that rhyme and say them with your child.

TIME TO RHYME

Say the names of the pictures with your child. Have your child circle the pictures that rhyme with mat. Cross out the other pictures.

SLUMP OR JUMP

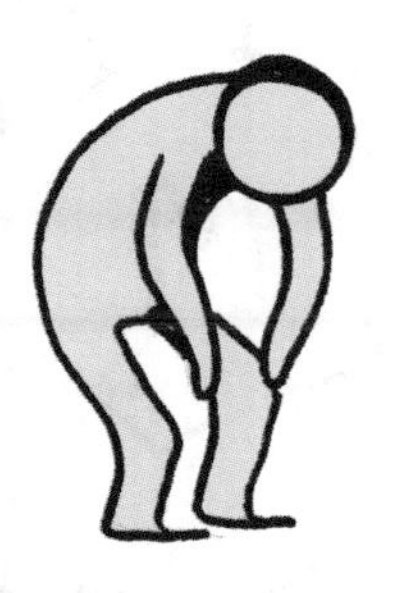

Review words that rhyme with "dog" by playing a game called "Slump or Jump."

Rhyming cards to cut out are located in the back of the book. Parent holds up picture cards, one at a time. The main word is "dog." Parent says the word. If it rhymes with "dog," your child jumps! If it does not rhyme, your child slumps down in his/her chair. Use several correct cards mixed with incorrect ones.

More Rhyming Games begin on page 208.

The pictures are cat, fish, hat, gnat, lemon.

Practice Heavenly Writing and then trace the Ms.

Do the maze with your finger first and then in pencil.

Mm MY MOM

Draw and color a picture of Mom.

"This letter says /m/." Say the /m/ words, letting your child repeat them.

MOTHER, MAY I?

"TAKE 4 BABY STEPS"

If you forget your manners and don't ask permission, you must go back to the beginning.

Other Steps:
Giant, Backwards, Bunny Hop

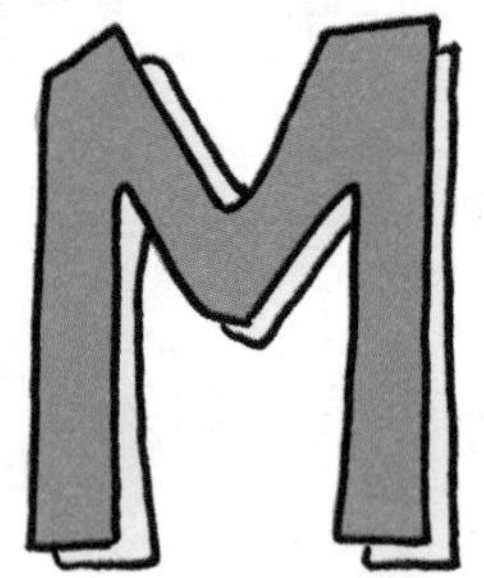

Say the name of the first picture in each row. Cross out the picture in each row that does not match the first picture.

FEED THE MONKEY!

Glue the monkey face from the Appendix on a box. Cut the box partially to "open" the monkey's mouth. Have your child feed the monkey with M pictures in the appendix. Note: Include two or three distractor cards.

The pictures are medal, map, monkey, moon, mom.

Hail Mary, full of Grace

Pray for us! In the year 1830, Mary promised to St. Catherine Labouré that she would send many graces to those who ask for them, and to those who wear her Miraculous Medal. Look at a Miraculous Medal closely with your child. Teach your child to pray "O Mary, conceived without sin, pray for us who have recourse to thee."

ANGEL, ANGEL, CAN WE CROSS YOUR GOLDEN BRIDGE?

The Angel stands on the bridge, sidewalk, or stretch of yard. The other players stand on one side of the "bridge" and say "Angel, angel, can we cross your golden bridge?" She answers: "Only if you have on the color ____________!"

Players who are wearing that color may cross the bridge easily. Players not wearing that color must try to run across the bridge and evade the angel. Whoever is caught is the next angel.

MIX AND MATCH

Another way to reinforce the naming of colors: have your child match items by color. Use blocks, cards, or toy cars.

V MAKING VOLCANOES

BACKYARD VOLCANO

Form a volcano in the dirt or sand with a cup inside at the top. Fill the cup with 1 teaspoon baking soda. Add a few drops of red food coloring to a 1/4 cup of vinegar and pour into the baking soda cup. Stand back!

Practice Heavenly Writing and then trace the Vs.

V V V V

Color the picture.

PINK about THIS

Add a few drops of red food coloring to white frosting or softened cream cheese. Let your child mix it up and spread on a plain cookie or piece of bread.

Vv SING TO YOUR VALENTINE

Color the bird.

GOD GAVE YOU A VOICE

God gave you a voice to praise His name and say nice things to others. Use your voice to whisper, sing, and shout some words that begin with /v/.

"This letter says /v/." Say the /v/ words, letting your child repeat them.

Say the names of the pictures with your child.
Circle the pictures that begin with /v/.

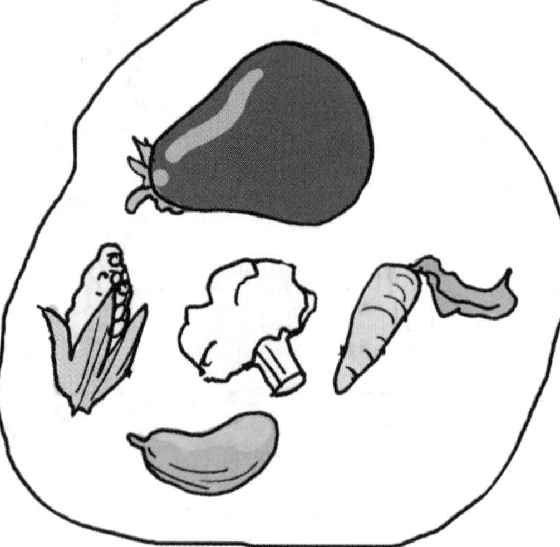

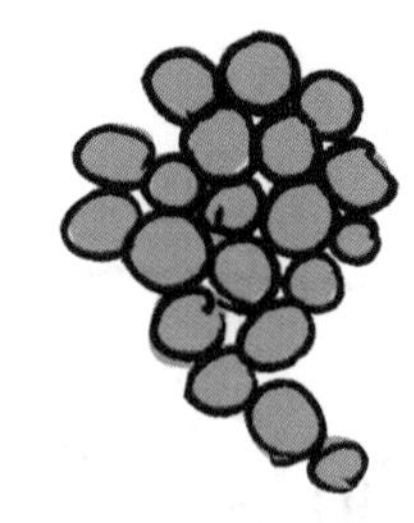

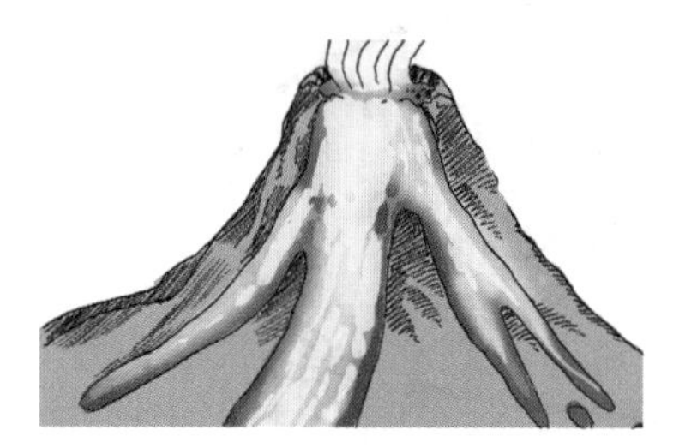

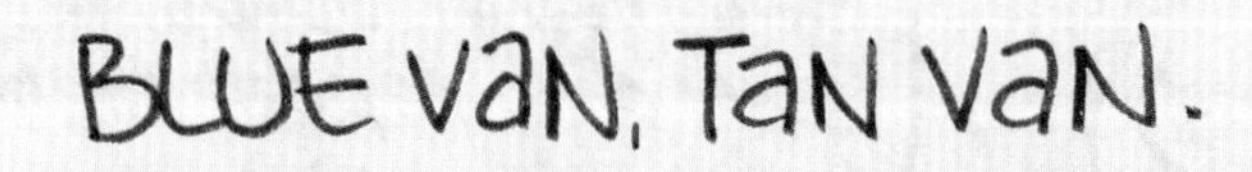

Let your child count the vans that you see, either when walking or driving.

The pictures are van, iguana, vinegar, grapes, volcano, cow.

GOD MADE MY SENSES

WHAT'S NEW IN UNIT 5

- The Letters J, G, and Q
- The Sounds /j/, /g/, and /q/
- Language Development
- Tracing Triangles
- Rhyming "Wing"
- Environmental Sound Discrimination
- Identify Body Parts that Correspond with Each of the Five Senses

GOD MADE MY SENSES

THANK YOU, GOD!

Help your child to color the rainbow.

RED
ORANGE
YELLOW
GREEN
BLUE
PURPLE

IN PRAISE AND THANKSGIVING

Talk about the things you see, hear, smell, taste, and touch.

Say a little prayer with your child: "Thank you, dear God, for my skin that feels soft like my blanket."

BEHOLD THE RAINBOW! THEN BLESS ITS MAKER, FOR MAJESTIC INDEED IS ITS SPLENDOR; SIRACH 43:11

GOD GAVE ME EYES TO SEE

Point to the matching tools.

BLIND MAN'S BLUFF

Set up a room with obstacles: hassock, pillows, table to crawl under. Go through it sighted. Then try it wearing a blindfold!

CAN YOU SEE WHAT I SEE?

TURNING TO HIS DISCIPLES IN PRIVATE, HE SAID, BLESSED ARE THE EYES THAT SEE WHAT YOU SEE. LUKE 10:23

LORD, THANK YOU FOR GIVING US EARS TO HEAR ALL THE SOUNDS WE LOVE: BIRDSONG, LAUGHTER, SINGING, MUSIC, RUNNING STREAMS, RAIN.

Can You Hear what I Hear?

Draw a line from the boy to the things you can hear.

Sounds Like...

One person stays out of sight to make the noises, while the other person guesses what he is hearing. Shake bells, make animal noises, hit a pan lid with a spoon.

I CAN HEAR GOD'S WORD

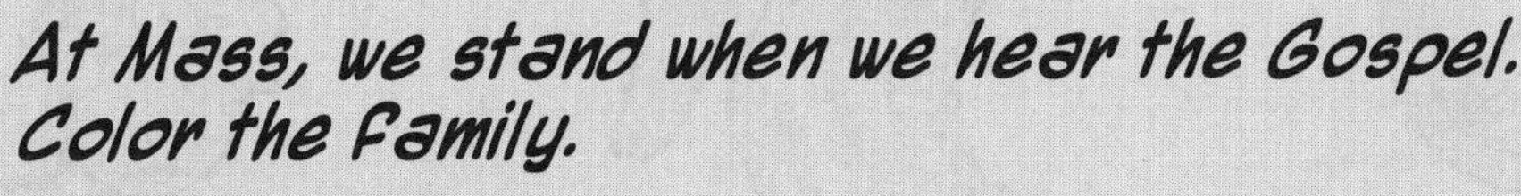

At Mass, we stand when we hear the Gospel. Color the family.

BIBLE STORY

Read a favorite Scripture story to your child from the Bible, not a story book. Handle the Bible with reverence. Light a candle while you read. Try Luke 18: 15-17

WHAT I SAY TO YOU IN THE DARKNESS, SPEAK IN THE LIGHT; WHAT YOU HEAR WHISPERED, PROCLAIM ON THE HOUSETOP. MATTHEW 10:27

Can You Hear Me Now?

How many instruments can you name?

I LOVE a PARADE!

Make a pair of maracas from dry, empty water bottles. Add some dried rice or dried beans and seal the top with masking tape. Play some marching music, grab some more noisemakers, and start the parade!

J Jesus Loves Me

Draw a picture of yourself near Jesus. Look for Js as you come to them in this unit or in print.

Practice Heavenly Writing, and then trace the Js.

. . . JESUS CALLED FOR THE CHILDREN, SAYING:
LET THE LITTLE CHILDREN COME TO ME. . . LUKE 18:16

Jj JUMP, JOKE AND JUGGLE

"This letter says /j/." Say the /j/ words, letting your child repeat them.

HUNTING FOR J

Have a /j/ snack, with juice and jelly on crackers. Go on a /j/ hunt, placing sticky notes with the letter J on items that start with /j/.

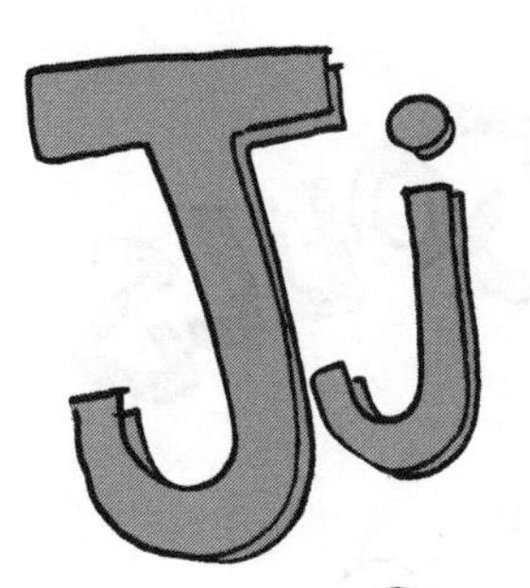

Draw lines from left to right to connect the matching pictures that begin with /j/.

HEADS BOW

Teach your child to bow his head at the name of Jesus.

The pictures are juggler, juice, jack-in-the-box, jump, Jesus.

Jj A JOLLY WAY TO WIN SOULS

JOKED AND

.

HIS JOLLY WAY LED

TO

JESUS .

Color the pictures.
Find the Js.

Help your child "read" the rebus pictures as you read the sentences and point with your finger, left to right. Listen for the /j/ words.

JUNIOR JUGGLER

To develop eye-hand coordination, try tossing a beanbag or ball from one hand to another.

GOD GAVE ME A NOSE TO SMELL

THANK YOU, GOD!

SMELLS LIKE...

Collect items to smell: cinnamon, orange, and coffee. Repeat the names of the items as you present them. Let your child sniff each item and talk about it. Does it smell good? Sweet? Sour?

THINGS I CAN SMELL

Help your child to trace the triangles

During the day, say a quick, out-loud prayer with your child (when you smell something nice) like "Thank you, God, for the smell of dinner cooking."

TRY THIS TRIANGLE

Let your child make a triangle out of three straws or three uncooked spaghetti noodles.

TIME TO RHYME

Say the names of the pictures with your child. Have your child circle the pictures that rhyme with wing. Cross out the other pictures.

RHYMING BASKET

Collect small items. You can say, "Wencil, can you find something that rhymes with wencil?" Child picks out the pencil. You can use any object because the rhymes may be real or nonsense rhymes.

For reinforcement, use Rhyming Cards from the back of the book to play the Rhyming Games that begin on page 208.

The pictures are sing, banjo, king, horn, string.

MY NOSE KNOWS

Draw a line from the girl to the things you can smell.

Talk about how our noses can alert us - something burning, milk that has gone sour.

The pictures are flashlight, flower, rainbow, soup, skunk, switch.

LARGE and SMALL POTS and PANS

Put a circle around the small things.
Put a line under the larger things.

DINNER'S READY!

Let your child help when you are cooking something on the stove, or in the oven. Then send him to another part of the home to play. Ask him to come tell you as soon as he can smell the item cooking.

G GREEN GRAPES

Color the green grapes.

Practice Heavenly Writing and then trace the Gs.

Make Gs in salt.

G G G G

A GAGGLE of GEESE

Color and count the geese.

"This letter says /g/." Say the /g/ words, letting your child repeat them.

Place items or pictures that begin with /g/ on a table. Play a guessing game. "I am thinking of a fruit that starts with /g/ and is sweet to eat."

Say the name of the first picture in each row. Cross out the pictures in each row that do not match the first picture.

GO, GREEN, GO!

Have some races! Let your starter use a green cloth or green paper when he shouts "Go!"

The pictures are goose, grapes, girl, glove, globe.

GOD GIVES ME FOOD TO EAT

Color the picture.

How many loaves? __________

How many fishes? __________

Read and retell the story about the multiplication of the loaves and fishes. (Mark 6:34-44) Use the Bible and light a candle while you read.

LORD JESUS, YOU ATE AND TASTED MANY GOOD THINGS: BREAD, FISH, AND WINE. YOU BLESSED THEM AND GAVE THEM TO PEOPLE WHO WERE HUNGRY.

GOD GAVE ME A TONGUE TO TASTE

Talk about your child's favorite things to taste. Parent: print as child dictates.

SALTY, SWEET, OR SOUR?

Place small pieces of vegetables, fruit, cereal, and crackers on a plate. Have your child close his eyes and try them. Do they taste sweet, sour, or salty?

PLEASING WORDS ARE A HONEYCOMB, SWEET TO THE TASTE AND HEALTHFUL TO THE BODY. PROVERBS 16:24

HOT and COLD

Circle hot things with red.
Circle cold things with blue.

Let your child fill a tea kettle or a mug with cold water. Heat the water on the stove, or microwave it. Watch for the steam.

Q QUEEN'S QUILT

Color the pictures.

QUARTERS N THE QUART JAR

Practice Heavenly Writing and then trace the Qs.

Try saving quarters in a jar to give to the poor.

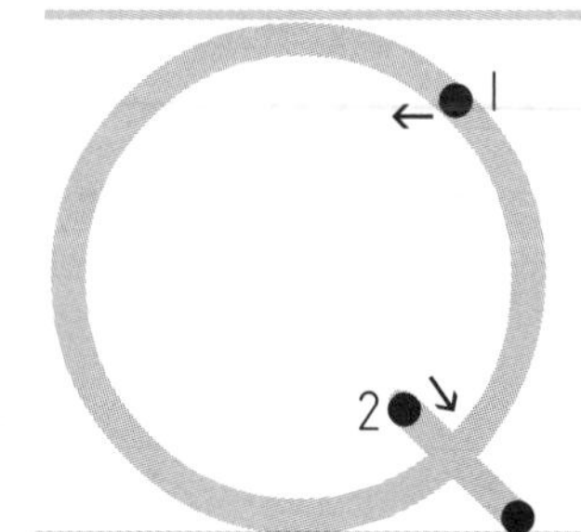

Qq QUIZ ME!

"THE ANSWER IS...
QUEEN"

QUAIL

QUEEN

?

QUESTION MARK

Color the girl.

"This letter says /q/ (qu)."
Say the /q/ words, letting your child repeat them.

THE Q GAME

Give some clues to prompt the answer that begins with Q.

"Her husband is the King."
or
"What's another word for fast?"

On a separate sheet of paper, trace your child's hand. Have him tell you five things he can touch. Print them on each finger.

FEELS LIKE...

Using a basket of clean laundry, pull out each item and let your child feel it before you fold it. Help your child use the adjectives soft, smooth, scratchy, and hard. This is a good opportunity to teach folding skills.

DEAR GOD, YOU HAVE GIVEN US WONDERFUL HANDS AND SKIN TO USE OUR SENSE OF TOUCH. THANK YOU.

Qq

Say the names of the pictures with your child. Circle the ones that begin with /q/.

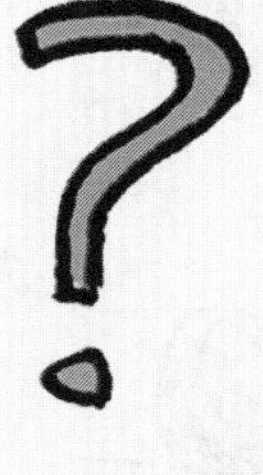

How many cups?

Let your child use a measuring cup and water to fill a quart jar or pitcher.

The pictures are question, quiver, banjo, quail, quilt, switch.

MATCH BY SIGHT, THEN TOUCH

Draw a line from left to right to connect the matching pictures.

It's in the bag!

Collect pairs of small items (as above). Place one set in a sock or bag. Show your child one item, then have her feel in the bag for the matching item.

The pictures are acorn, candy, block crayon, game piece.

I CAN DO WONDERFUL THINGS

WHAT'S NEW IN UNIT 6

- The Letters D, P, and R
- The Sounds /d/, /p/, and /r/
- Concepts of More/Less
- Rhyming "Dog," "Play"
- Movement Concepts
- Comparison of Distances, Quantities

I CAN DO WONDERFUL THINGS

Keep a running list of things your child can do now that he couldn't do when he was a baby.

I CAN. . . .

I'M GROWING UP!

Reminding children of all they can do is an important confidence builder.

LORD, YOU HAVE MADE MY CHILD, WHO HAS GROWN SO MUCH SINCE INFANCY. THANK YOU FOR ALL THAT SHE CAN AND WILL DO. HELP ME TO TEACH HER TO KNOW YOU, LOVE YOU, SERVE YOU, AND TO LIVE IN YOUR GRACE. AMEN.

BLESSED THE PEOPLE . . .WHO WALK IN THE RADIANCE OF YOUR FACE, LORD.
PSALM 89:16

Color the duck.

Print Ds and a few other letters on paper plates or cardboard. Place them on the floor. Children dance while you play music, and like Musical Chairs, when the music stops, children run to step on a "D."

Practice Heavenly Writing and then trace the Ds.

1↓ →2

D D D D

Dd VISITING THE DONUT DUCK

Color the picture.

"This letter says /d/."
Say the /d/ words letting your child repeat them.

DUCK, DUCK, GOOSE!

Play Duck, Duck, Goose.

If you are short on players try enlarging your circle with dolls or stuffed animals.

GOD HELPS ME TO BE STRONG AND HEALTHY.

Date: ______________________

I can run. How fast? _______

I can walk. How far? _______

I can play. What game? _______

I can jump. How high? _______

If this is a challenge for your child, then write down what he is able to do: smile, sit or stand.

Parent: Cut out the food in the appendix on page 229 and help your child to glue the food on the plate.

ON TODAY'S MENU

Go to myplate.gov and print out a placemat of good food.

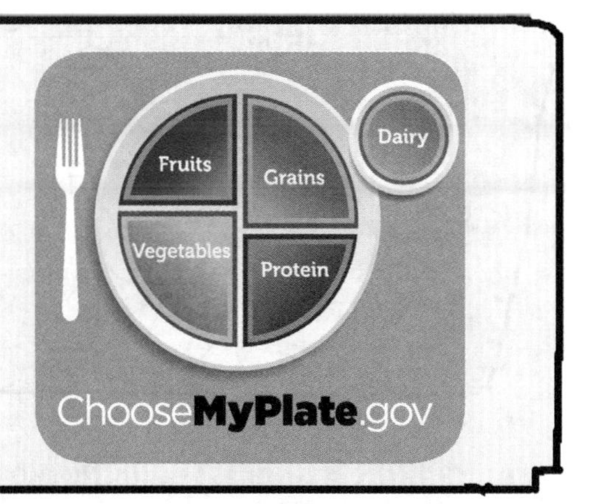

I CAN CHOOSE HEALTHY FOODS

Draw a line from the healthy foods to the boy.

HELPING IN THE KITCHEN

Have your child help scrub potatoes for a meal.

The pictures are carrots, candy, chicken, cake, apple, lime drink, toast.

Say the name of the first picture in each row. Circle the picture in each row that matches the first picture.

Making Change

Place a sheet of paper over a dime and other coins. Help your child rub over them with the side of a pencil or crayon. Count the rubbings when done.

The pictures are dog, daisies, duck, dad, dance.

I TALK WITH WORDS

THANK YOU, GOD!

Color the turtle.

Can you tell a story about what is happening in the picture?

THE POWER OF ENCOURAGEMENT

Praise your child for his good efforts:
"Lucy set the table all by herself today!"
"Jason helped Mary with her Math."
"Mark played with the baby while Mom showed Sarah the alphabet."
It's so valuable for our children to be praised and encouraged for their good deeds.

LET YOUR SPEECH ALWAYS BE GRACIOUS, SEASONED WITH SALT, SO THAT YOU KNOW HOW YOU SHOULD RESPOND TO EACH ONE. COLOSSIANS 4:6

TIME TO RHYME

Say the names of the pictures with your child. Have your child circle the pictures that rhyme with dog. Cross out the other pictures.

Try this new game!

Parent says a word. Take turns giving rhyming words. The one giving the last word wins. Silly words are acceptable as we are training the ear to recognise the rhymes.

For reinforcement, use Rhyming Cards from the back of the book to play the Rhyming Games that begin on page 208.

The pictures are frog, hog, carrots, jog, and candy.

Practice Heavenly Writing and then trace the Ps.

P P P P

I can THINK. I can PRAY.

Talk to your child about prayer. Let your child dictate where she likes to pray. Let her watch you while you write it on the line below. Color the hour glass.

This is where I like to pray: ____________________

MY PRAYER PLACE

Help your child prepare a special prayer place with a statue, doily, or rosary.

BUT WHEN YOU PRAY, GO TO YOUR INNER ROOM, CLOSE THE DOOR, AND PRAY TO YOUR FATHER IN SECRET. MATTHEW 6:6

I USE THESE TO HELP ME PRAY

Color the basket.

LISTENING FOR GOD

Silence is necessary for thoughtful prayer. Help your child to practice silence by using a three-minute egg timer. Help him choose a quiet space.

Place a holy card, small crucifix, or special picture and the egg timer in a small basket. Teach him to sit quietly, and ask the rest of the family to respect the silence when someone else is praying.

VIVA IL PAPA!
"This letter says /p/." Say the /p/ words, letting your child repeat them.
Color the picture.
PEDDLER'S PACK
Use a crib sheet, or baby blanket. Search the house for items that begin with the sound of /p/. Let your child place them in the blanket, tie it up like a peddler's pack and show his wares, pretending to try to sell them!

TIME TO RHYME

Say the names of the pictures with your child. Have your child circle the pictures that rhyme with play. Cross out the other pictures.

For reinforcement, use Rhyming Cards from the back of the book to play the Rhyming Games that begin on page 208.

The pictures are pray, say, turtle, hay, quilt.

I CAN PRAY TO GOD BY MYSELF

Finger print candle flames with yellow. Count the candles.

VISIT CHURCH DURING HOLY HOUR

Explain to your child that Jesus is present in the beautiful golden monstrance.

Make a holy "10 minutes" instead of a holy hour. Bring something specific for your child to pray with or to look at, such as a small photo album with holy cards.

REJOICE ALWAYS. PRAY WITHOUT CEASING.
IN ALL CIRCUMSTANCES GIVE THANKS,
FOR THIS IS THE WILL OF GOD FOR YOU IN CHRIST JESUS.
1 THESSALONIANS 5:16–18

Draw lines from left to right to connect the matching pictures that begin with /p/.

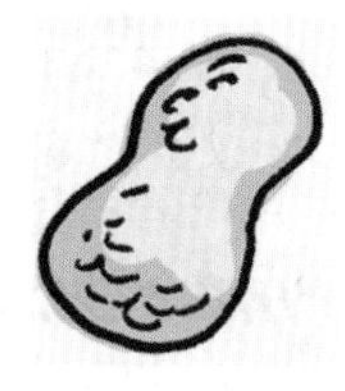

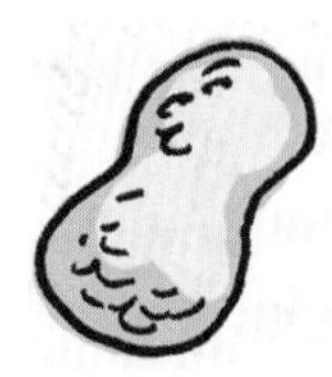

PIGGY PICKED A PERFECT PICKLE

Make up a silly sentence or tongue twister with words that begin with P. How about foods like pizza, popcorn, pineapple, pudding, popsicle, and pie?

The pictures are pumpkin, pie, pitcher, peanut, pizza.

Rr Rose and Rosary

Color the picture.

Relay Racers

Collect R items & some Non-R items. Place in a pile some distance from the starting line. Child races to the pile, retrieves an R item and returns to starting line. Repeat until all R items are removed.

Practice Heavenly Writing and then trace the Rs.

R R R R

Rr Rooster's River Raft

Color the rooster.

"This letter says /r/."
Say the /r/ words letting your child repeat them.

"ALL ABOARD!"

Make a railroad track and a road on an old shower curtain or large piece of paper. Find /r/ things to go on the road or rails. Toy trains which carry an /r/ load (bag of rice, box of raisins) are allowed. Red cars are allowed too! A toy rabbit is allowed to hop on the road, so is a robin.

Pick a simple response that is sung or said at Mass. Practice at home.

Praise your child for joining in when it's time to pray at Mass.

I WILL BE GLAD AND EXULT IN YOU; I WILL SING PRAISE TO YOUR NAME, MOST HIGH. PSALM 9: 3

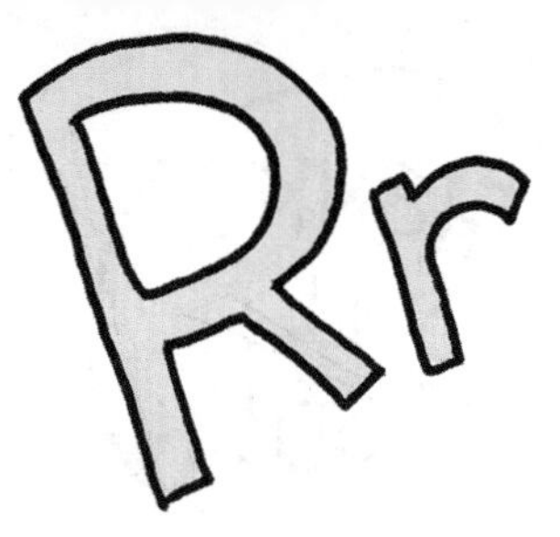

Say the names of the first picture in each row. Cross out the pictures in each row that do not match the first picture.

I'LL EAT MY WORDS

Parent: Print R on a napkin or paper plate. Give your child a few raisins. Cover the letter R with the raisins before eating them.

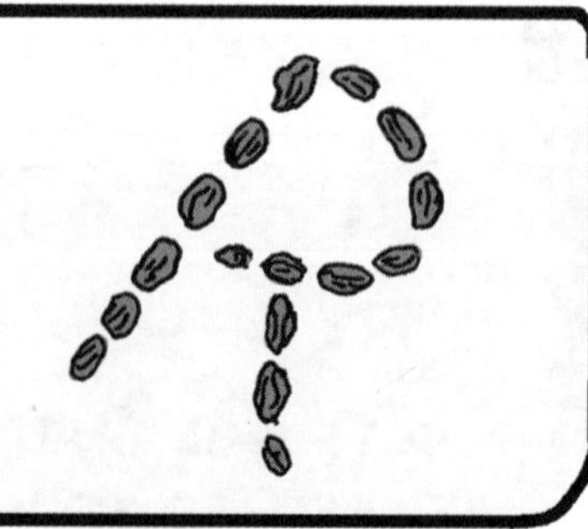

The pictures are rabbit, radish, raisins, robin, rose.

GLORY TO GOD IN THE HIGHEST!

SINGING LIKE ANGELS

Read the Nativity Story (Luke 2:1-4). Explain how the angels first sang "Glory to God in the Highest" and that we sing or say that same song now at Mass. Take time to teach your child some phrases from the Gloria so that she can sing or say it during Mass.

WHAT GOES TOGETHER?

Draw a line between the tools that we use together.

MY CATHOLIC CHURCH

WHAT'S NEW IN UNIT 7

- The Letters K, N, S, and W
- The Sounds /k/, /n/, /s/, and /w/
- Word Awareness
- Rhyming "Socks"
- Tracing Cross

MY CATHOLIC CHURCH

Underline the word "Church" with a blue crayon on this page and through the unit.

Paste a photo of your church on this page.

HOLY TIME

Craft: Draw a simple outline of a monstrance using a plate and a ruler. Have your child paint the outline yellow. Glue a doily on top. Then glue on a paper circle to represent the Host.

LORD, HOW BEAUTIFUL IS YOUR DWELLING PLACE. THANK YOU FOR YOUR REAL PRESENCE IN OUR CATHOLIC CHURCH. HELP ME TO TEACH MY CHILD THAT YOUR CHURCH IS A HAVEN, A PLACE OF WORSHIP, A HOLY PLACE BECAUSE YOU ARE THERE.

MY CATHOLIC CHURCH HAS MANY CROSSES

The Cross is a sign that reminds us how much Jesus loves us.

SO THEY TOOK JESUS, AND CARRYING THE CROSS HIMSELF HE WENT OUT TO WHAT IS CALLED THE PLACE OF THE SKULL, IN HEBREW, GOLGOTHA. JOHN 19:16–17

MY CATHOLIC CHURCH HAS A CRUCIFIX

Trace the rays.

MY PRAYER FOR JESUS

Say a simple prayer when you see a crucifix. "Jesus, I love you." "Christ has died. Christ is risen. Christ will come again." In church, look at the Stations of the Cross. Find the Crucifixion.

HE HUMBLED HIMSELF, BECOMING OBEDIENT TO DEATH, EVEN DEATH ON A CROSS. PHILIPPIANS 2:8

K JESUS IS MY KING

Trace the rays and color Jesus.

KING OR QUEEN FOR A DAY

Make a paper crown and embellish with a "K." Play King and do good things for your subjects like choosing a good lunch.

Practice your Heavenly Drawing and then trace the Ks.

1 2 3

K K K K

Kk Kittens and Kites

"This letter says /k/."
Say the /k/ words letting your child repeat them.

Make This Kite

Make and fly a kite! Simple version: tie the end of a spool of thread through the handles of a plastic grocery bag. Put an unsharpened pencil through the spool, and take your kite outside on a windy day.

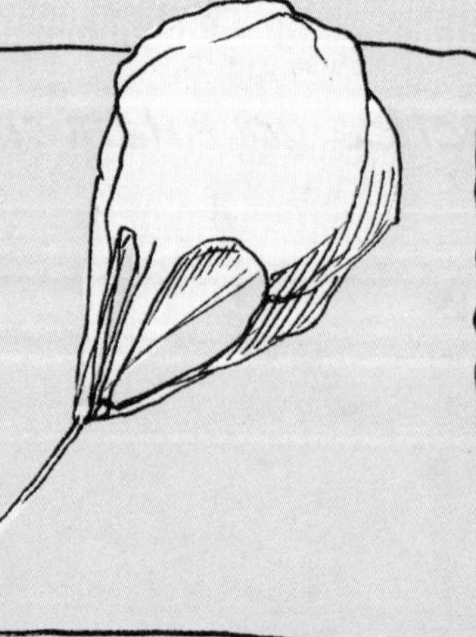

I GENUFLECT TO JESUS BECAUSE HE IS MY KING, MY LORD, MY GOD.

Color the picture. Clap the syllables in the words gen-u-flect, rev-er-ent.

EVERY KNEE SHALL BEND

Ask your child to watch you or an older child genuflect on the right knee. Have your child practice this gesture of respect, which we give to Jesus our King. Do it slowly and reverently.

THAT AT THE NAME OF JESUS EVERY KNEE SHOULD BEND, OF THOSE IN HEAVEN AND ON EARTH AND UNDER THE EARTH, AND EVERY TONGUE CONFESS THAT JESUS CHRIST IS LORD, TO THE GLORY OF GOD THE FATHER. PHILIPPIANS 2:10–11

Say the names of the pictures with your child. Circle the pictures that begin with /k/.

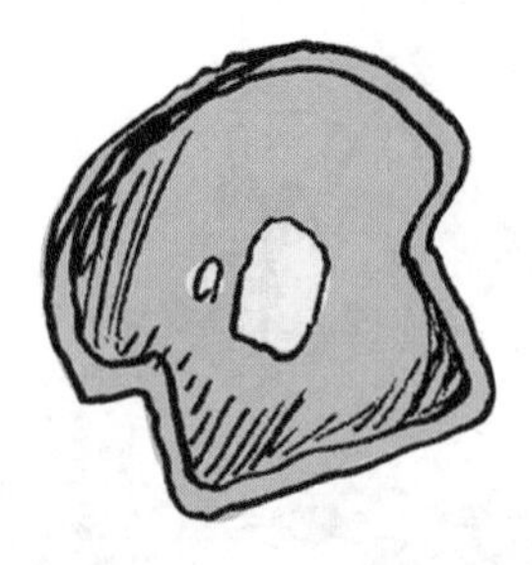

Pack like a kangaroo!

Make a kangaroo pouch: use a large T-shirt and fasten.

Have child hop like a kangaroo with a "Joey" in her pocket. Play kangaroo for a day.

The pictures are kangaroo, toast, kick, kitten, lego.

MY CATHOLIC CHURCH HAS A

HOLY WATER FONT

Color the holy water.

A holy water font is used in Catholic churches as a way to remember our baptismal promises.

IN THE NAME OF THE FATHER

Help your child make the Sign of the Cross. Place a sticker or draw a cross with a marker on the right hand to help your child remember to use that hand.

NOW, WHY DELAY? GET UP AND HAVE YOURSELF BAPTIZED AND YOUR SINS WASHED AWAY, CALLING UPON HIS NAME. ACTS 22:16

IN CHURCH, BOYS AND MEN REMOVE THEIR HATS AS A SIGN OF RESPECT.

Color the boy's cap and the man's hat.

WITH DUE RESPECT

Practice gestures of respect with your child: kneel, genuflect, bow, make the Sign of the Cross.

MY CATHOLIC CHURCH

HAS A TABERNACLE. JESUS IS PRESENT IN THE TABERNACLE.

Color the tabernacle yellow.

MY MOST SPECIAL THINGS

Decorate a small box in which to keep your most special things.

LORD, I LOVE THE REFUGE OF YOUR HOUSE, THE SITE OF THE DWELLING-PLACE OF YOUR GLORY. PSALM 26:8

THE TABERNACLE HOLDS A CIBORIUM

The ciborium holds the bread that has become Jesus.

Color the Ciborium.

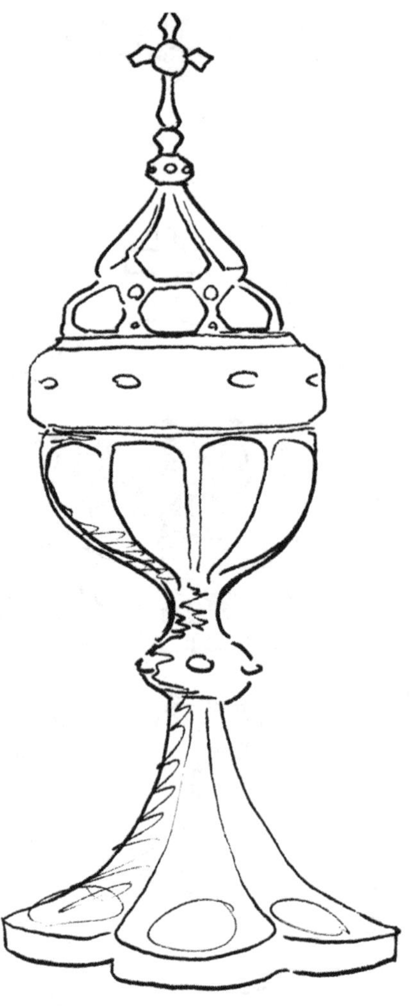

Look for the tabernacle when you visit different Catholic churches. Point out the ciborium when Father takes it out to distribute Communion.

JESUS SAID TO THEM: I AM THE BREAD OF LIFE. . . JOHN 6:35

MY CATHOLIC CHURCH

HAS A SANCTUARY LAMP TO SHOW THAT JESUS IS THERE.

Color the sanctuary lamp red.

JESUS IS MY LIGHT

When you visit any Catholic church with your child, point out that if the red sanctuary lamp near the tabernacle is lit, it means Jesus is present.

JESUS SPOKE TO THEM AGAIN, SAYING, 'I AM THE LIGHT OF THE WORLD. WHOEVER FOLLOWS ME WILL NOT WALK IN DARKNESS, BUT WILL HAVE THE LIGHT OF LIFE.' JOHN 8:12

N NINE NUNS and a NOVICE

Color the white habit blue.

DEAR SISTER

Has your child ever met a nun? Look for Catholic monasteries or convents. Write a note asking them for permission to visit.

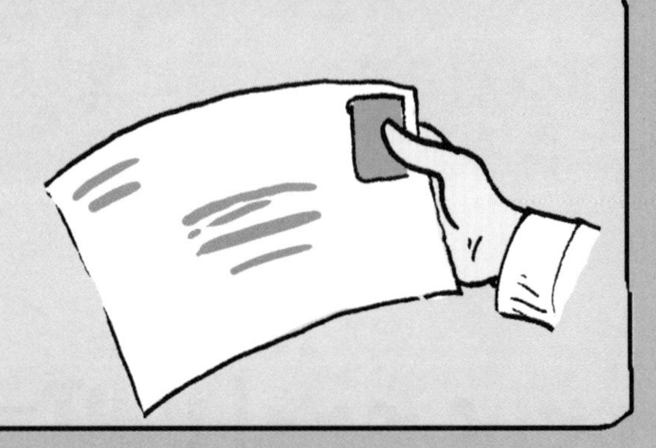

Practice Heavenly Writing and then trace the Ns.

FOR WHOEVER DOES THE WILL OF MY HEAVENLY FATHER IS MY BROTHER, AND SISTER, AND MOTHER. MATTHEW 12:50

Nn THE BEST NEST IN THE WEST?

Circle the Ns.

"This letter says /n/." Say the /n/ words letting your child repeat them.

I HAVE THE BEST NEST.

Here's a great rainy day activity. Help your child make a nest with blankets and pillows.

MY CATHOLIC CHURCH

HAS A STATUE OF THE BLESSED VIRGIN MARY, THE MOTHER OF JESUS.

Color Mary's robe blue. Count the flowers.

Teach your child to pray the Ha
Mary or the Angelus.

. . . THE ANGEL GABRIEL . . . SAID UNTO HER: HAIL, FULL OF GRACE, THE LORD IS WITH THEE: BLESSED ART THOU AMONG WOMEN. LUKE 1:26–28

Draw lines from left to right to connect the matching pictures that begin with /n/.

Make a necklace by stringing wooden beads onto a pipecleaner. Yarn works well if you stiffen one end with tape.

The pictures are nun, nest, newspaper, nickel, nuts.

Color the picture.

It's a good idea to have your child practice letters in ways he can touch and feel.

This sensory method reinforces the shape of the letter for him.

Practice Heavenly Writing and then trace each S.

S S S S

MY CATHOLIC CHURCH

HAS A STATUE OF ST. JOSEPH, THE FOSTER FATHER OF JESUS

Color and count the votive candles.

PATRON OF FAMILIES

Say a prayer in front of the St. Joseph statue in church. Light a candle there.

. . . JOSEPH, THE HUSBAND OF MARY. OF HER WAS BORN JESUS WHO IS CALLED THE MESSIAH. MATTHEW 1:16

Ss Sun and Sand

"This letter says /s/."
Say the /s/ words letting your child repeat them.

Color the sun.

SOCK PUPPET!

Puppets are a great way to teach and reinforce many skills: Greeting other children, introducing themselves, using "Please" and "Thank you", taking turns, and sharing.

Sometimes it's fun when the puppet gets it the wrong way, and your child can correct the puppet!

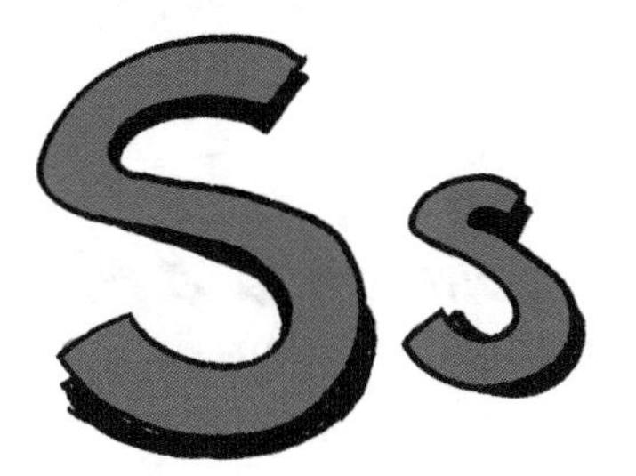

Say the name of the first picture in each row. Cross out the pictures in each row that do not match the first picture.

The pictures are snowman, squirrel, sock, star, and scissors.

TIME TO RHYME

Say the names of the pictures with your child. Have your child circle the pictures that rhyme with socks. Cross out the other pictures.

Run around Sockball. Make a modified baseball diamond. If inside, use throw pillows, or furniture for bases. Adult pitches a sock ball (rolled up socks) to child. He must shout out something that rhymes with socks, and throw the sockball back to the pitcher in order to run to first base. Keep score of how many home runs are made!

For reinforcement, use Rhyming Cards from the back of the book to play the Rhyming Games that begin on page 208.

The pictures are fox, snowman, box, juice, pitcher, blocks.

Ww Walking with the Whale Wagon

Color the picture.

Jump on this Wagon

Make a wagon using a box (wheels are optional). Attach a rope to pull it and let your child give wagon rides to his toys and stuffed animals.

Practice Heavenly Writing and then trace the Ws.

1 2 3 4

WALRUS IN A WATERMELON WHEELBARROW

"This letter says /w/." Say the /w/ words letting your child repeat them.

Color the watermelons

WHAT THE WALRUS WANTS

Glue or tape the Walrus face from the Appendix on a box. Cut the box partially so that you can "open" the walrus's mouth. Have your child feed the walrus with items that start with /w/. Children love to hear the Walrus "roar" when they are successful.

Say the name of the first picture in each row. Circle the picture in each row that matches the first picture.

Read the story of Jonah from a Picture Bible or read it from your family Bible and retell it to your child.

Help your child make a "belly" by covering a table with a blanket and let him play Jonah.

The pictures are wagon, window, watermelon, whale, wheelbarrow.

Color the pictures.
Find the Ws.

A LITTLE BOY LOOKED OUT HIS 

.

HE (WATCHED) THE RAIN FALLING ON HIS (WAGON).

HE (WALKED) OUTSIDE IN THE PUDDLES OF 

AND SAW LOTS OF (WORMS).

Help your child "read" the rebus pictures as you read the sentences and point with your finger, left to right. Listen for the /w/ words.

SIMPLY SPECIAL

Sometimes on a rainy day it's a simple pleasure to sit on a comfy sofa, surround yourself with books and have a special story time with Mom or Dad.

HELPERS FOR GOD

WHAT'S NEW IN UNIT 8

- The Letters X, Y, and Z
- The Sounds /x/, /y/, and /z/
- Rhyming "Cot," "Ran," "Door"
- Tracing a Word

ANGELS are HELPERS FOR GOD

Have your child tell you how someone helped him today. Help him to compose a simple thank you.

Parent writes and child signs and decorates.

. . .BEHOLD, THE ANGEL OF THE LORD APPEARED TO JOSEPH IN A DREAM AND SAID, 'RISE, TAKE THE CHILD AND HIS MOTHER, FLEE TO EGYPT, AND STAY THERE UNTIL I TELL YOU.' MATTHEW 2:13 A

ANGELS PROTECT US.

Count and color St. Joseph's footprints.

Gather your nativity set figures and then read aloud Matthew 2:13-15.

As you read the Scriptures, let your child move the figures. Begin with the Holy Family sleeping and the angel appearing to Joseph. Then Joseph wakes Mary, they quickly pack, and they take Baby Jesus to safety.

JOSEPH ROSE AND TOOK THE CHILD AND HIS MOTHER BY NIGHT AND DEPARTED FOR EGYPT. MATTHEW 2:14

SAINTS ARE HELPERS FOR GOD

Now in Heaven, they love to help us here on earth.

My Patron Saint is: ______________________

St. Thérèse of Lisieux taught us her "Little Way" of loving Jesus in everything we do, even washing pots and pans. Teach your child about little sacrifices for love, like sharing a toy or treat.

Thread 3-5 pieces of cereal on a string.

Hang horizontally so your child can reach it.

He moves one piece each time he does a sacrifice for Jesus.

ST FRANCIS OF ASSISI was a HELPER FOR GOD

Francis was a rich young man but being rich did not make him happy. He gave away all that he owned to God's poor. Then Francis was happy.

TRUE TREASURE

Help your child go through toys or clothes and choose some to give away. This is a way to build up treasure in Heaven.

WHEN JESUS HEARD THIS HE SAID TO HIM,
'THERE IS STILL ONE THING LEFT FOR YOU: SELL ALL THAT YOU HAVE AND DISTRIBUTE IT TO THE POOR, AND YOU WILL HAVE A TREASURE IN HEAVEN. THEN COME, FOLLOW ME.' LUKE 18:22

TIME TO RHYME

Say the names of the pictures with your child. Have your child circle the pictures that rhyme with cot. Cross out the other pictures.

Stir three sets of rhyming cards in a pot. Put out three bowls. Pull out one card at a time and place in bowls according to the rhyming family. Serve with a smlle!

The pictures are pot, medal, dot, tot, van.

What did the Bear have for Dinner?

Help your child trace the answer.

FISH

Teach your child to play Tic-Tac-Toe

Practice Heavenly Writing, and then trace the Xs.

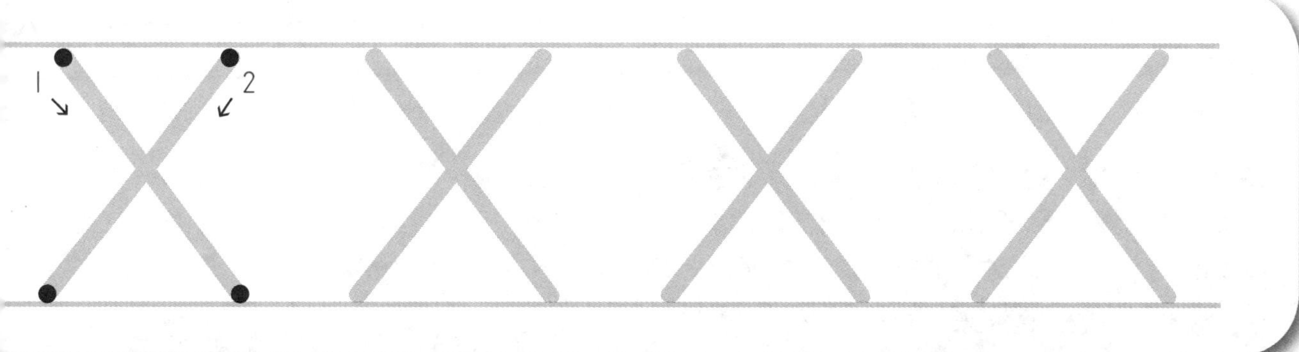

Xx a BOX OF SIX FOXES
Count and color the foxes.
"This letter says /x/.
See the box? Box ends with the /x/ sound." Say the other words and let your child repeat them.
X MARKS THE SPOT
Child decorates a box with x's.
Parent or older sibling makes a treasure map of one or more rooms with X "marks the spot" on the map and hides the box.

Say the name of the first picture in each row. Listen for the sound /x/ at the end of the words. Cross out the picture in each row that does not match the first picture.

Help your child mix something today like oatmeal, salad or pancakes.

The pictures are fox, box, mix, ox, fix.

PRIESTS ARE HELPERS FOR GOD

Talk about the pictures with your child. What is Father doing? How is he being a helper for God?

Take time after Mass to see Father and say hello and thank you.

GO, THEREFORE, AND MAKE DISCIPLES OF ALL NATIONS, BAPTIZING THEM IN THE NAME OF THE FATHER, AND OF THE SON, AND OF THE HOLY SPIRIT, MATTHEW 28:19

JESUS was a ELPER IN HIS FAMILY.

Discuss the picture with your child. What is Jesus doing? How did He help in His family?

ave your hild point ɔ the ːatching ɔols.

BRIGHT AND SHINY

Spray a little furniture polish on a cloth for your child. Teach him how to polish the furniture.
Help your child to clean a window within his reach.

HE WENT DOWN WITH THEM AND CAME TO NAZARETH,
AND WAS OBEDIENT TO THEM; AND HIS
MOTHER KEPT ALL THESE THINGS IN HER HEART. LUKE 2:51

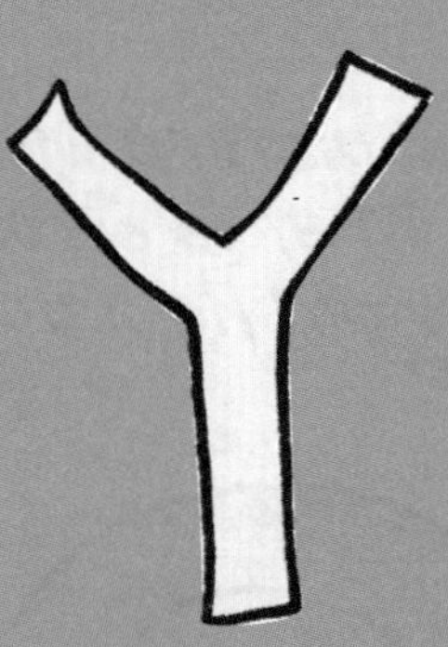

Color the jar.

YES!

YELLOW

YARN

Practice Heavenly Writing and then trace the Ys.

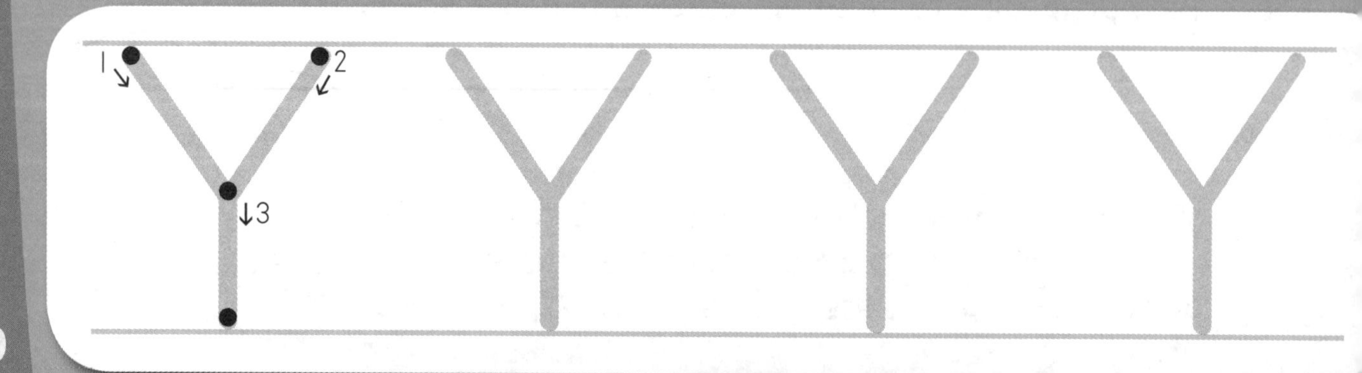

Yy Yodeling York and his Yellow Yak

Finish coloring the grass.

"This letter says /y/." Say the /y/ words letting your child repeat them.

Start a plant by placing a yam in a water-filled jar. Suspend the yam using three toothpicks. Keep it on a windowsill to capture the light and watch it grow.

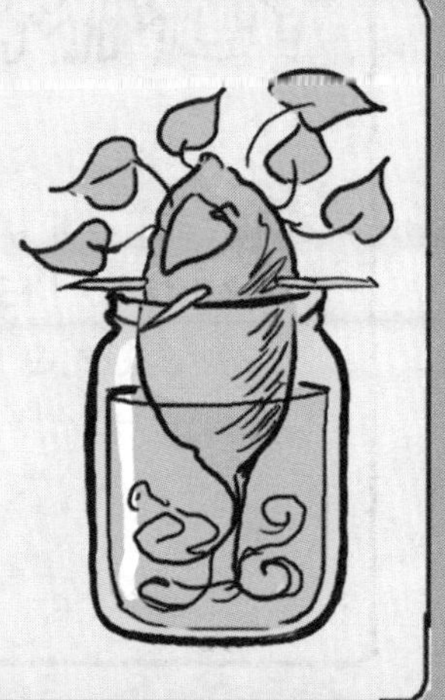

Draw lines from left to right to connect the matching pictures that begin with /y/.

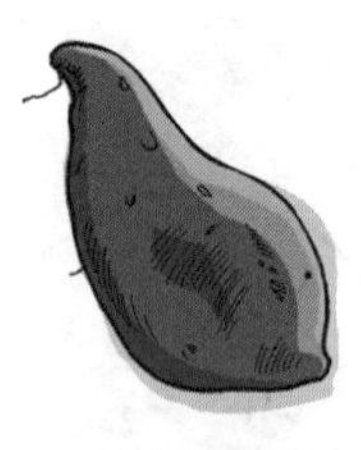

YUMMY YAMS

Cut a yam into thin slices and then into matchstick strips. Serve as a raw vegetable with a dip. Yum!

The pictures are yellow, yarn, yak, yam, yes.

SISTERS AND BROTHERS ARE HELPERS FOR GOD

Draw a line from the religious to what they do for God.

Talk with your child about the pictures. What are the sisters and brothers doing? How are they being helpers?

Make a picture collage of brothers and sisters. Keep it in your prayer place and pray for vocations!

SO WHEN HE HAD WASHED THEIR FEET
[AND] PUT HIS GARMENTS BACK ON AND RECLINED AT TABLE AGAIN,
HE SAID TO THEM, . . . "AS I HAVE DONE FOR YOU,
YOU SHOULD ALSO DO." 1 JOHN 13:12- 15

Z a ZOO FULL OF ZEBRAS

Color the zoo wall.

LEARN YOUR ZIPCODE

Parent using highlighter, write your Zip Code and help your child trace the numbers.

____

Practice your Heavenly Writing and then trace the Zs.

1 2 3

Z Z Z Z

Zz Zeke and his Zany Zippers

"This letter says /z/." Say the /z/ words letting your child repeat them.

ZIP ALONG!

Make zigzag lines on a chalkboard or large piece of paper. Make small toy cars zoom along the zigzag roads.

Say the name of the first picture in each row. Circle the picture in each row that matches the first picture.

WHO'S AT THE ZOO?

Build a zoo with blocks, boxes and stuffed animals.

The pictures are zebra, zero, zigzag, zip code, zither.

I CAN BE A HELPER TO MY FAMILY.

Draw a line from the messy items on the floor to show where things should go.

CHILDREN, LET US LOVE NOT IN WORD OR SPEECH BUT IN DEED AND TRUTH. 1 JOHN 3:18

TIME TO RHYME

Say the names of the pictures with your child. Have your child circle the pictures that rhyme with ran. Cross out the other pictures.

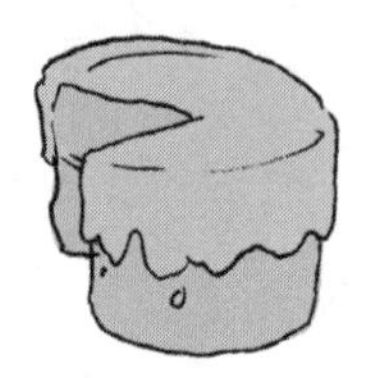

RAN

TIME TO FIND THE RHYME

Cut out the "an" cards from the appendix. Place one face up in the middle and the rest face down in a circle around it. Include 3 or 4 distractor cards.

Take turns turning a card over. "If it rhymes, you get to keep it. If it doesn't, place it in a discard pile. Whoever has the most cards wins!"

The pictures are van, cake, man, sofa, pan.

FAMILIES are HELPERS FOR GOD

Discuss this picture with your child.
How is this family helping God?
Draw 6 cookies on the plate.

"HI NEIGHBOR!"

Take a treat to a neighbor or draw a picture for their refrigerator.

DO NOT NEGLECT HOSPITALITY, FOR THROUGH IT SOME HAVE UNKNOWINGLY ENTERTAINED ANGELS. HEBREWS 13:2

CHILDREN are HELPERS FOR GOD

Talk to your child about what is happening in the picture. Who is being a helper for God?

Point to the matching items. Find the pictures that rhyme (door, store, four) and color the picture.

ON THE LOOKOUT

God gives us many opportunities to be His helpers. We need only keep our eyes and ears open and be ready to help.

FOR THIS IS THE MESSAGE YOU HAVE HEARD FROM THE BEGINNING: WE SHOULD LOVE ONE ANOTHER, 1 JOHN 3:11

TIME TO RHYME

Say the names of the pictures with your child. Have your child circle the pictures that rhyme with door. Cross out the other pictures.

String up a "clothes line" and attach rhyming words to the line.

Pinching a clothes pin so it opens builds finger strength and dexterity, which is needed for printing.

The pictures are four, bee, pour, eggplant, more.

RHYMING ROUNDUP

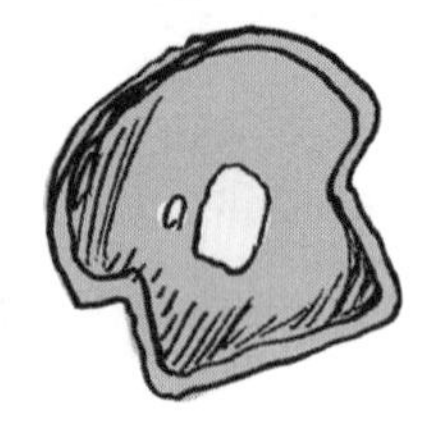

The pictures are:
fan, can, dog, man,
tot, dot, pot, box
pray, play, hay, boy,
four, more, toast, door.

In each row, cross out the picture that does not rhyme.

HEADING TO THE CARD CORRAL

Outline corrals on the floor with yarn or string. Shuffle 2-4 sets of rhyming cards and wrangle your rhyming cards into the right corral.

Congratulations on a job well done!

____

Name

has successfully completed

Early Literacy for Young Catholics

Pre-Kindergarten Activity Book

by Seton Home Study School

As of this date ____________________

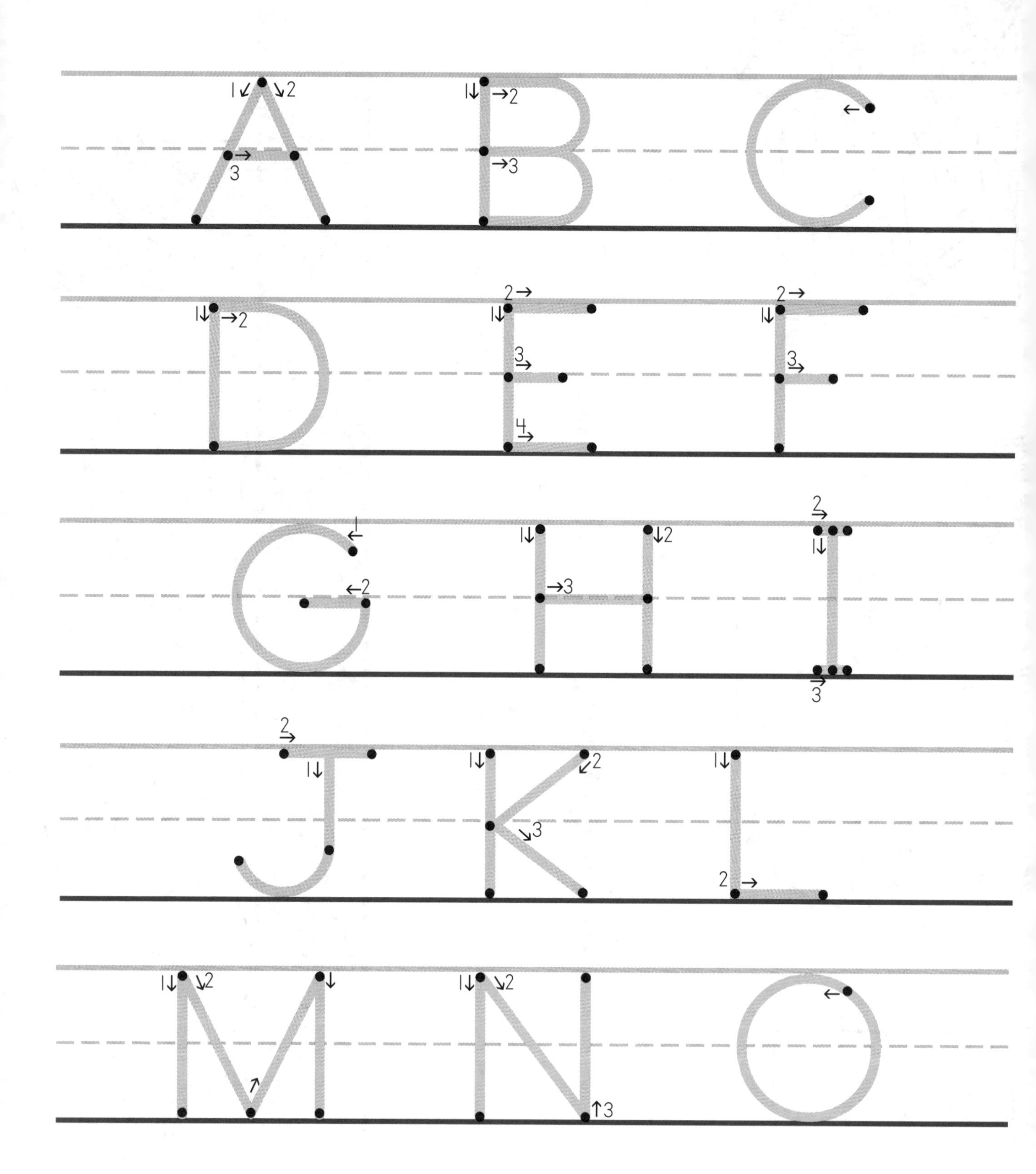

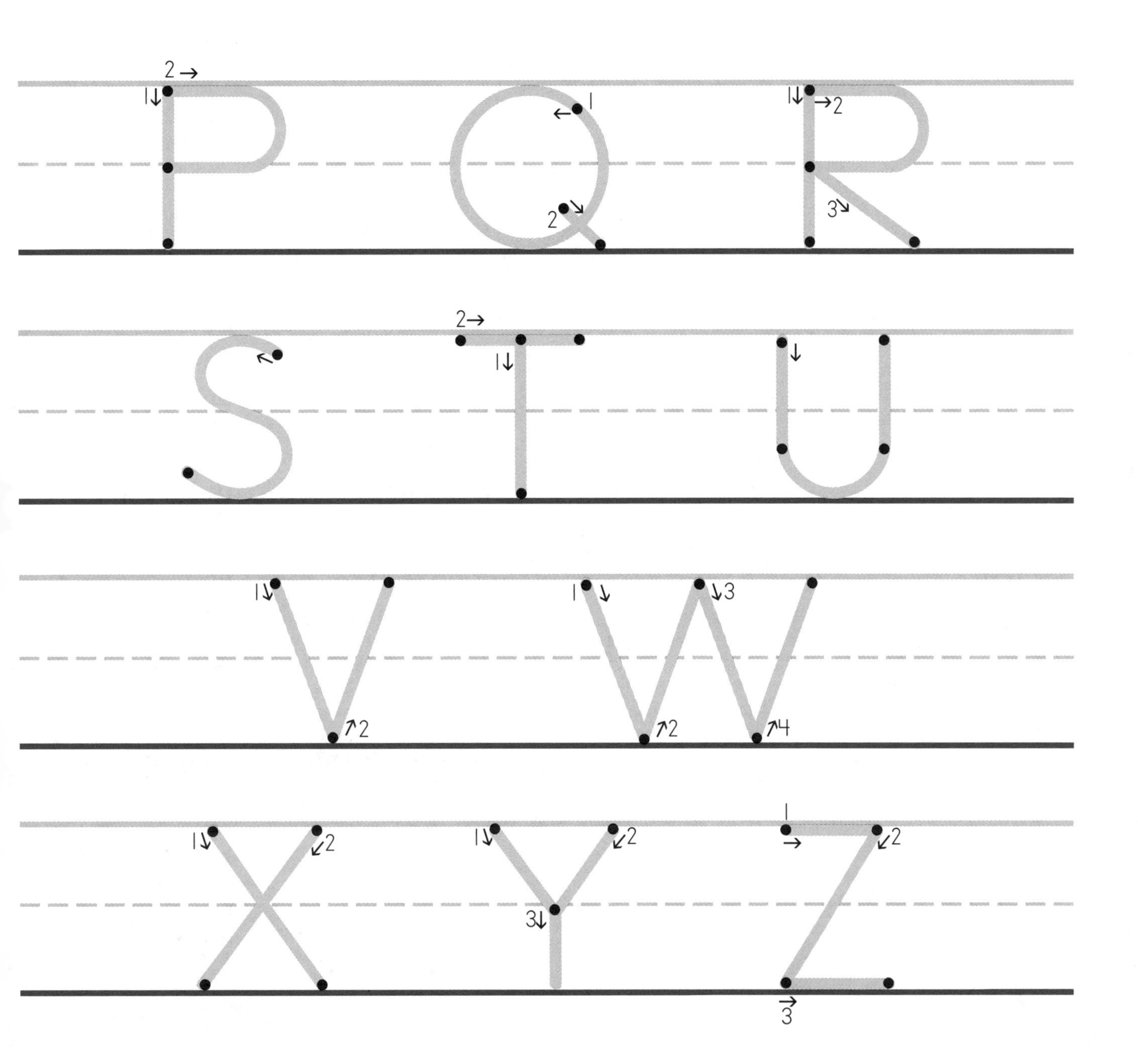
2 →
1↓
← 1
2 ↘
1↓
→2
3↘
↖
2→
1↓
↓
1↓
↗2
1 ↓
↓3
↗2
↗4
1↓
↙2
1↓
↙2
3↓
1
→
↙2
→
3

Pronunciation Guide

Basic

a
cap
cape
ah (ah)
all (awe)

b
ball

c
cat
cent

d
dad (not /duh/)

e
bed
be

f
fan

g
get (not /guh/)
gem (not /juh/)

h
he

i
sit
site
piano

j
jam (not /juh/)

k
kite (not /kuh/)

l
let

m
mom

n
no

o
got (ah)
go (oh)
do
off (awe)

p
pope (not /puh/)

qu
quiz (/kw/)

r
red (not/er/ruh/)

s
sat
as

t
ten (not /tuh/)

u
us (uh)
use (you)
truth
put

v
van

w
we (not /wuh/)

x
ox (/ks/)

y
yes (not /yuh/)
hymn
my
baby

z
zoo

FREQUENTLY ASKED QUESTIONS

GET READY! Some General Questions

Why are the letters not introduced in ABC order?

The letters are not introduced in alphabetical order, but rather based on the ease of the strokes required to make them. The activity book itself begins with pages where your child can scribble, and can trace simple vertical, horizontal, and circular lines.

Does my child need to know all the letters and sounds?

No. Although all the letters and sounds are introduced, this year is a year of ***exposure*** to, not mastery of the entire alphabet. *Virginia's Foundation Blocks for Early Learning: Comprehensive Standards for Four-Year-Olds* (2013) states that at the end of the year prior to Kindergarten, a four year old child should be expected to:

- ❑ correctly identify between 10-18 uppercase alphabet letters by name in random order.
- ❑ select a letter to represent 8-10 sounds. "Which letter says the sound /b/?"
- ❑ give the common sound for 5-8 letters. "What does the letter M say?"

What is a tripod grasp?

A tripod grasp is the correct way to hold a pencil, crayon, chalk, or marker for the smoothest use. Most very young children begin to hold writing utensils with their whole fist. The correct grasp must be taught. Basically, the writing utensil is held between the thumb and pointer finger, while resting on the middle finger. The ring and pinky fingers are tucked under.

Giving a child small (3"or less) pieces of crayon, or chalk with which to draw or color is a way to encourage use of the three fingers to grasp. Children should have practice manipulating small objects (legos, tinkertoys) in order to develop the muscles necessary to grasp correctly a writing utensil. Pencil grips, which may be helpful, are available at teacher supply stores.

What is "clapping to syllables?"

Clapping to syllables is a way to help your child to listen, as well as to begin to break down a word into phonetic syllables. Say the word: Guard–i-an, and clap as you say each syllable. After practice, your child will be able to tell you how many claps are needed.

Any word can be used. Try the following:

Clap to children's names. Jes-si-ca, Mir-i-am, Jon-a-than
Clap Saints' names: Catherine, Teresa, Benedict, Dominic, Joseph Cupertino
Clap animal names: tiger, elephant, giraffe, ant
Clap church related words: Tabernacle, Altar, Benediction, Monstrance, genuflect
Clap some superheroes: Superman, Spiderman
Clap some princesses: Cinderella, Sleeping Beauty, Snow White

How do I teach initial sounds?

Note: / / around a letter means to say the sound of the letter. In teaching phonics, you need to differentiate the sound the letter makes from the letter name. You will see this throughout the book. Refer to the included sound pronunciation guide.

For each individual sound, introduce it by saying it clearly and close to your child, so she can see your mouth. For example, when introducing the sound for the letter B, say

"This letter says **/b/.**"

Show each picture to the child, emphasizing the initial sound.

"This is a **bird**. **Bird** starts with the **/b/** sound. Can you say it?"

"Listen to this word. **Baby** starts with the same sound as **bird.** Can you hear it?

They start with the same sound, **/b/**."

How do I teach rhyming?

Teaching rhyme is essentially teaching a very specific awareness of a unit of sound which is at the end of a word. Training the ear to "hear" rhymes is the first step. Children may begin to learn to recognize rhyming words between the ages of four and five, but it is not an easy concept. They have to play with sounds, and hear many rhymes before they can begin to pick them out, or provide rhyming words when asked.

Preschool is a time to introduce the concept, but it may not be mastered until later.

So, get out the Mother Goose books! Enjoy the age-old rhymes with your child.

Play recordings of children's songs and listen for the rhymes.

Read a rhyming book. Emphasize the words that rhyme and say them with your child.

Read children's poems out loud. See if your child can find the rhyming pairs.

Sing songs with your child, and listen for the rhyming words.

When reading nursery rhymes, say the second rhyming word quietly, and encourage your child to say it too. Then try leaving off the second rhyme, to see if your child can say it.

Some specific suggestions for later in the year:

1. Make up funny songs using two rhyming words, such as cat and hat.
Then to the tune of "Farmer in the Dell" make up a phrase and sing it.
"The cat sat on the hat, the cat sat on the hat, hi ho the Derry oh, the cat sat on the hat." Other variations could include:

"The man fell in the pan"
"The duck drove the truck"
"The fish swam in the dish"

2. Vary the above, by using the rhyming cards in the Appendix. After you have cut out several sets, try the following:

Hold up the pictures as you sing the song, or let your child point to them (make sure they are in the correct left to right order) while singing a silly phrase.

3. Give your child picture cards of 2 or 3 rhyming pairs. Make sure he can name the pictures. Have him sort them into rhyming pairs. Add more pairs as your child becomes more proficient.

4. Make a list of rhymes: Give your child the first word, "cat." Have him think of other words that rhyme with cat, and print them as he dictates them. It's reinforcing to draw or collect pictures of the rhyming words on the list.

5. Make a rhyming basket. Gather small items. Adult says "Wencil, wencil, can you find something that rhymes with wencil?" Child picks out the pencil. You can use any object, because the rhymes may be real or nonsense rhymes.

GET SET! A Little Extra Help

My child can't pronounce certain sounds correctly yet. What can I do?

The acquisition of specific sounds is highly variable in children. The following sounds: /f/, /l/, /r/, /s/, /th/, and /ch/ develop over a range of years. A four year old may be highly articulate, but on the other hand, may not correctly say some of these sounds until kindergarten or the early grades.

Please Note: Given that the /**s**/ sound is a later developing sound (the majority of children can produce the sound /s/ at age 6), many four year olds will be unable to accurately produce this sound in isolation or in context of a word. /th/ is a common substitution. You can give your child a clue – "Put your teeth together and blow." You can give your child a mirror so he can watch how he is forming the sound. However don't expect your child to use it in a word correctly especially if he cannot say the sound (produce it in isolation). However, a four year old has the auditory ability (auditory perception) to distinguish between the /s/ and the /m/ sounds when he hears them because they are very different. Don't worry about your child producing the sounds. Help your child to distinguish between the sounds.

My child doesn't seem to understand "same and different." What can I do?

Before attempting to teach different sounds, realize that:

- Children will learn the concept more easily with objects and pictures. Play matching games with your child. Start with eight cards from a memory game. Sort the silverware.
- Children need to transfer the concept of same and different from visual to auditory by discriminating between environmental sounds. Play some rhythm instruments out of sight. Can your child tell you if you've played the same one twice, or two different ones?
- Children need to transfer the concept of same and different from the concrete (environmental sounds) to the abstract: letter sounds.
- When teaching letter sound discrimination, children have an easier time if the sounds are completely different (/m/ and /b/) as opposed to being in the same group of sounds (/b/ and /d/).

My child's writing looks terrible. What can I do?

Begin with the large motor exercises. Control of the arm and shoulder muscles always precedes control of the hand and finger muscles. Heavenly writing, making strokes and scribbles (before doing letters) on large vertical surfaces (chalkboard, dry erase board, with a large paintbrush and water) are key experiences for all young children. You may not feel your child is ready for letter formation practice until January or later. Use a variety of the sensory activities suggested, making the letter in salt, rice, in shaving cream, with play dough, straws, and spaghetti noodles.

- A goal to reach by the *end* of the Pre-K program is for your child to print her first name independently, print 5-8 letters, and copy 3-5 letter words.

My child is having trouble cutting with scissors. What can I do?

Always supervise!

A child needs to have both hand strength and bilateral coordination to work with scissors. He should be able to maintain the correct grip when shown by an adult.

Scissors should be held in your child's dominant hand (The one he uses the most.) Different researchers have different opinions regarding the development of hand dominance. According to one expert, hand dominance doesn't emerge in many children until 3 years of age and is not well integrated until 8 or 9 years of age. If you are unsure of his dominant hand, watch which hand he typically uses to pick up cereal from a flat surface. Placement of an object affects what hand you reach with, so presenting items at midline (in the middle of the body) is a good idea.

Parents need to be good observers. If you give your child an activity that requires both hands, check to see which hand appears more coordinated. Sometimes one hand will have the power while the other one has the coordination. Parents can watch how their child is able to put small pegs in a peg board, how he manages tooth brushing, how he eats, how he throws a small ball. Hand dominance should not be forced. Your child will develop it. Children have good reasons for choosing which hand to use, and may not be consistent.

In the meantime, you should purchase left-handed scissors for a child who wants to use his left hand in cutting.

The thumb should be in the upper loop, and stay up. The middle and ring fingers can be in the lower, larger loop. The pointer finger is optimally used to support the scissors underneath, but may also be placed in the lower loop.

If your child can maintain this position, and begin to open and shut the scissors, he is ready to try holding the paper in his other hand, and begin snipping, or making random cuts in the paper.

An easy and satisfying task is for your child to snip small pieces from strips (1" wide) of paper which you have already cut for him. The paper bits can be saved for collages.

Once he is able to do these steps of random cutting and snipping, he may begin to make consecutive cuts with a forward movement.

Cutting on straight, very thick (1/2") lines is appropriate next.

The lines may be made gradually thinner, as he gains more control.

Later on, he will learn to cut out simple shapes with straight edges.

Finally, he will learn to cut on curved lines and to cut out circles.

My child has trouble naming colors. What can I do?

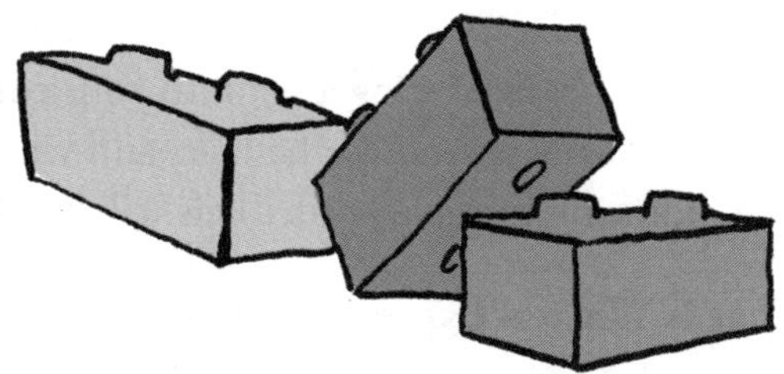

Children go through stages in recognizing color. It is always helpful to mention the color of objects when talking about them. "Let's play with the blue ball. Can you put on your red jacket?" Children learn much by hearing and association. Some four year olds have not mastered saying the names of colors correctly, so try these steps:

1. Match colors. A child should first learn to find the color which is the same. Have two red blocks, two blue ones, and two yellow ones. Place a red, a yellow, and a blue block on the table in front of your child. Show him your red one, and ask him to find the one which is the same. Continue with the yellow and blue ones. You can vary this activity with crayons, paint chips of basic colors from the paint store, socks, toy cars, whatever you can find around the home.

2. Sort objects by color. Give your child a variety of colored objects and help him to sort them into baskets or piles by color.

3. Use the method of receptive knowledge of color names. Put out an array of objects, and ask your child to find the yellow one. Find the red one.

4. Use the method of expressive knowledge of color names. Ask your child to tell you the color of an object.

Remember, start slowly and build. You may want to concentrate on one or two colors a month.

Go! Where can I go from here?

What is Oral Expression? How can I help develop it in my child?

Using words effectively in life is very important to all of us. Your four year old needs plenty of opportunities to talk and to listen to others – without interruptions, in order to master the fine art of turn-taking in conversations.

Seton's *Early Literacy for Young Catholics* Activity Book is designed to introduce new vocabulary in a natural and meaningful manner, both on the pages, and while trying the activities. Understanding a new word is best when it is connected to a real object or event. "Yolk" is more likely to be understood after breaking an egg, stirring it up, and making scrambled eggs.

Listening to stories is another important skill, and should happen once or twice a day. You should talk about the characters and about what's happening in the pictures with your child. Stop sometimes, and ask your child to tell you what he sees happening on the page and to predict what might happen next.

What is Print and Book Awareness? How can I help my child with this?

The first step is to visit the library and check out lots of books!

Show and use many kinds of print in your home in addition to books: the back of cereal boxes, cookbooks, newspapers, magazines, notes, lists, instruction booklets. Notice and comment on how and why you use all these materials. Exposing your child to a variety of print makes for a "print-enriched environment," which is essential to a preschool child beginning to learn about letters.

Before you begin reading a book to your child, take a few minutes to point out the front of the book, the title, and where you will read first. Move your finger from left to right across the page, pointing to each word. This will help her to "track" correctly in the future.

What is Written Expression? How can I help my child with this?

As suggested in this activity book, often write words down as your child dictates and watches. This teaches "spoken word to print correspondence." Encourage your child to "practice" by writing letters, greetings, signs, and lists while playing. Take these efforts seriously. This is important work for a preschooler. Children love little note pads and pencils. If you don't want to buy notepads, make some by cutting up scraps of paper and stapling them together to be order pads for playing restaurant, or shopping lists for pretend shopping. At this age, the act of writing (scribbling, doodling) is more important than the actual product. You want your child to feel confident in being able to practice this early form of written expression in order to make writing both useful and fun as he becomes more proficient.

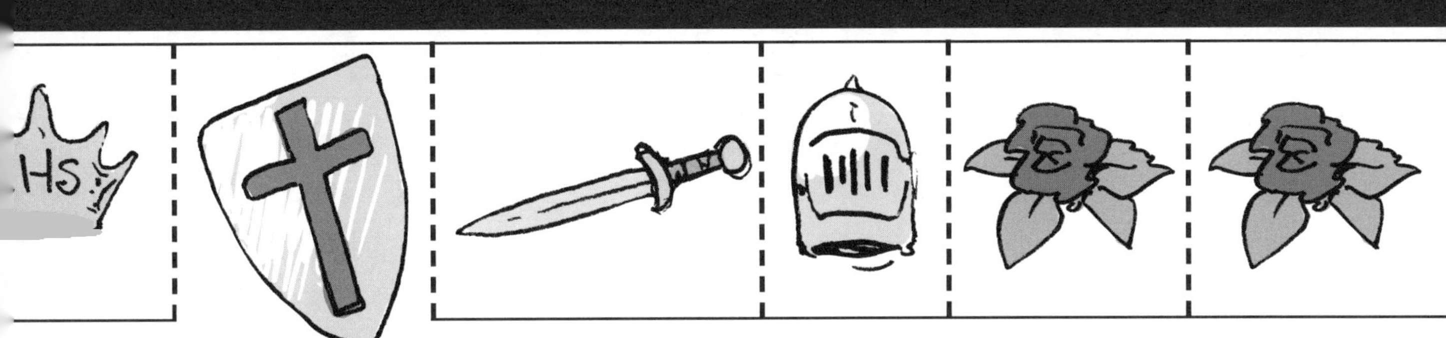

-ent: Cut the color strips and images
-ove. Have your child snip small squares
-l ornaments from the strips and help
- glue the pieces onto the stained glass
-dow in any design on page 21.

Parent: Cut out the pictures and help your child glue them on page 29.

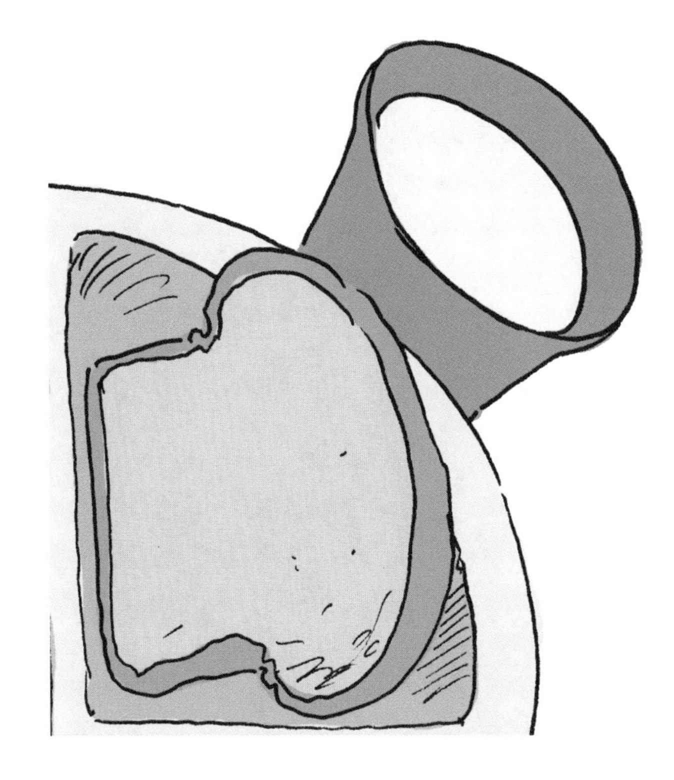

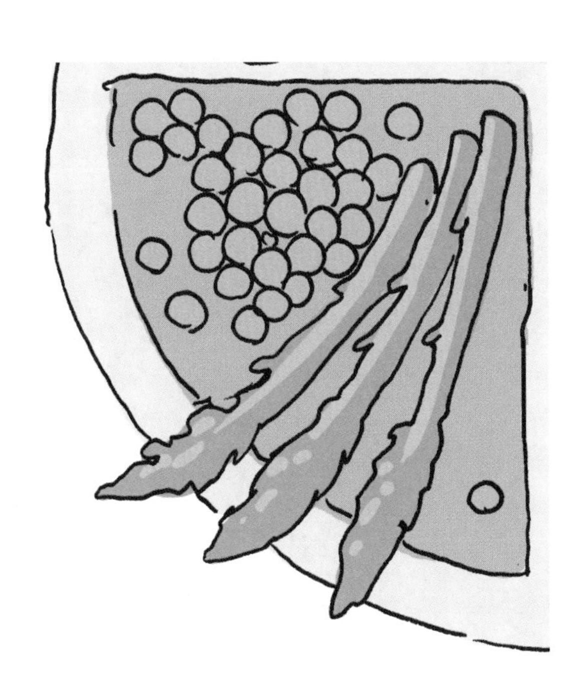

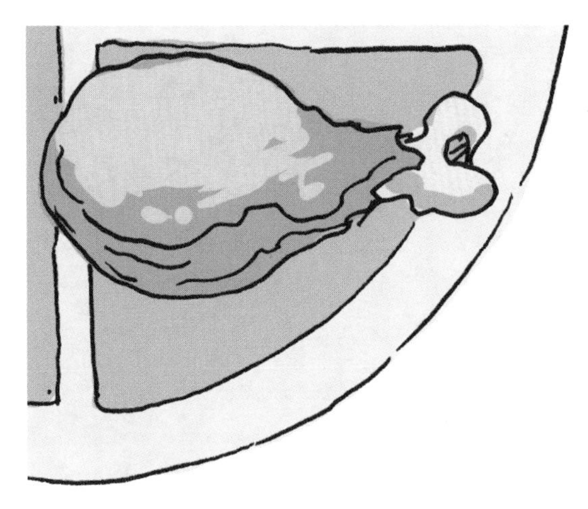

GOD GIVES ME HEALTHY FOOD TO EAT

Parent: Cut out the food groups on this page and help your child glue them to page 135.

TULIP
TOAST
TAPE
TUBA
TENT
TIMER

FEED the TIGER!

Early Literacy for Young Catholics
Seton Home Study School

LEMON
LOLLIPOP
LEAF
LUNCH
LUNCHBOX
LAMB
LADLE

FEED the LION

Early Literacy for Young Catholics
Seton Home Study School

MILK
MITTEN
MILK
MELON
MAP
X
MAP
MOON
MONEY

FEED the MONKEY

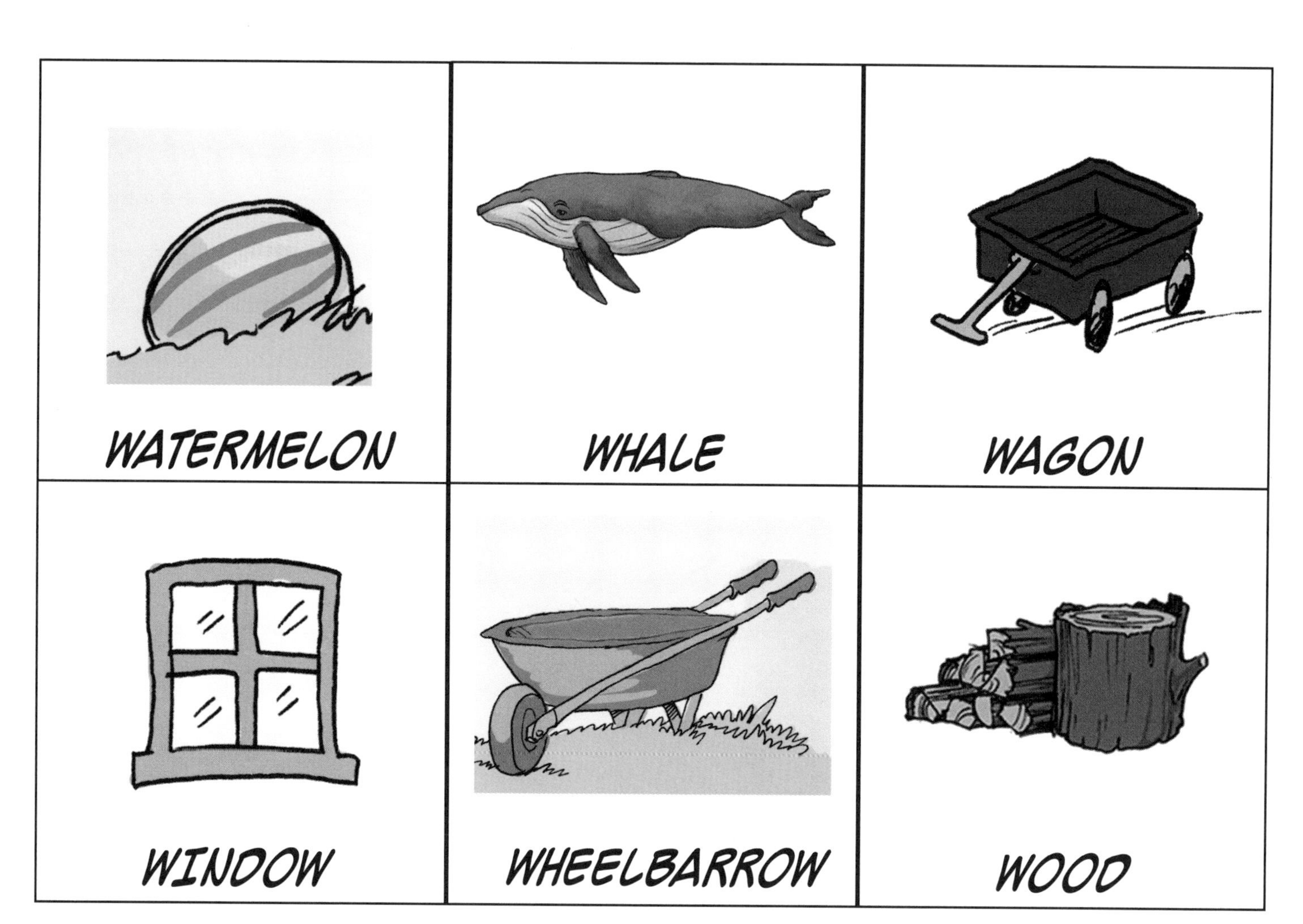
WATERMELON
WHALE
WAGON
WINDOW
WHEELBARROW
WOOD

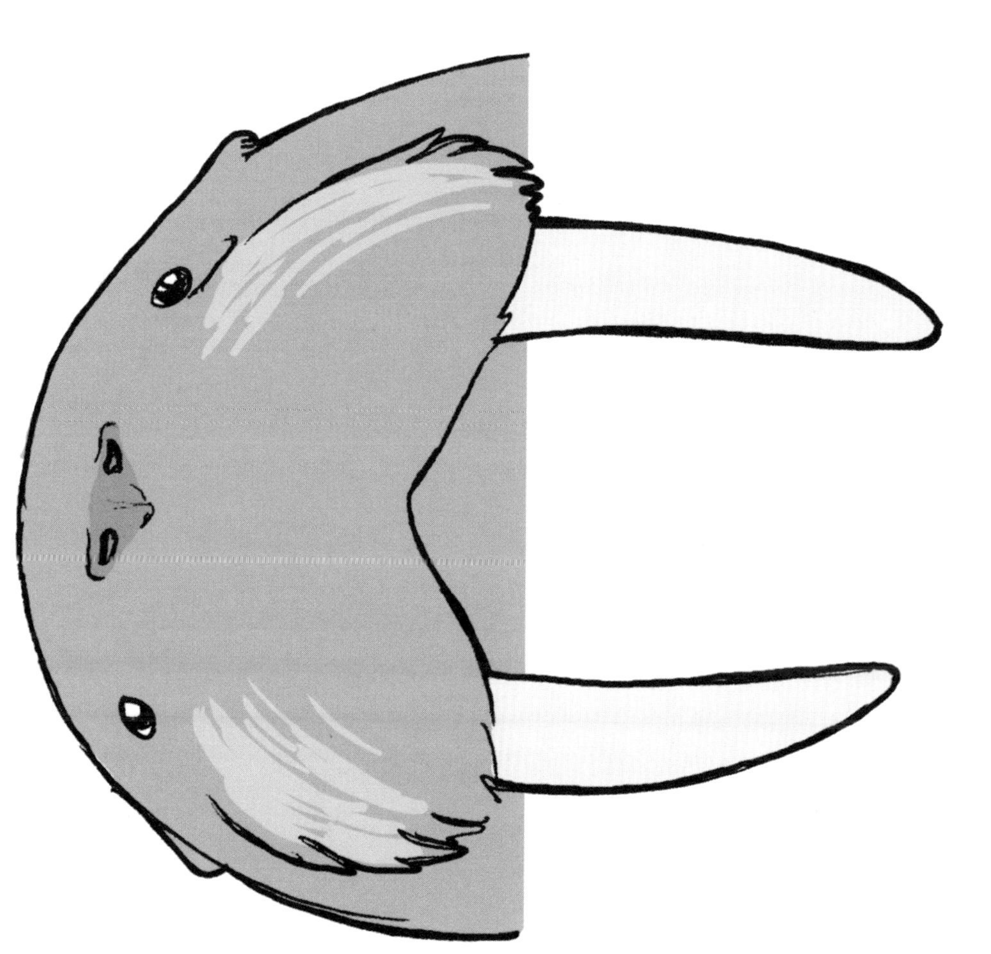

FEED the WALRUS

Early Literacy for Young Catholics
Seton Home Study School

Time to Rhyme: WING
WING
SING
KING
STRING
RING
Time to Rhyme: MAT
CAT
MAT
HAT
GNAT
BAT

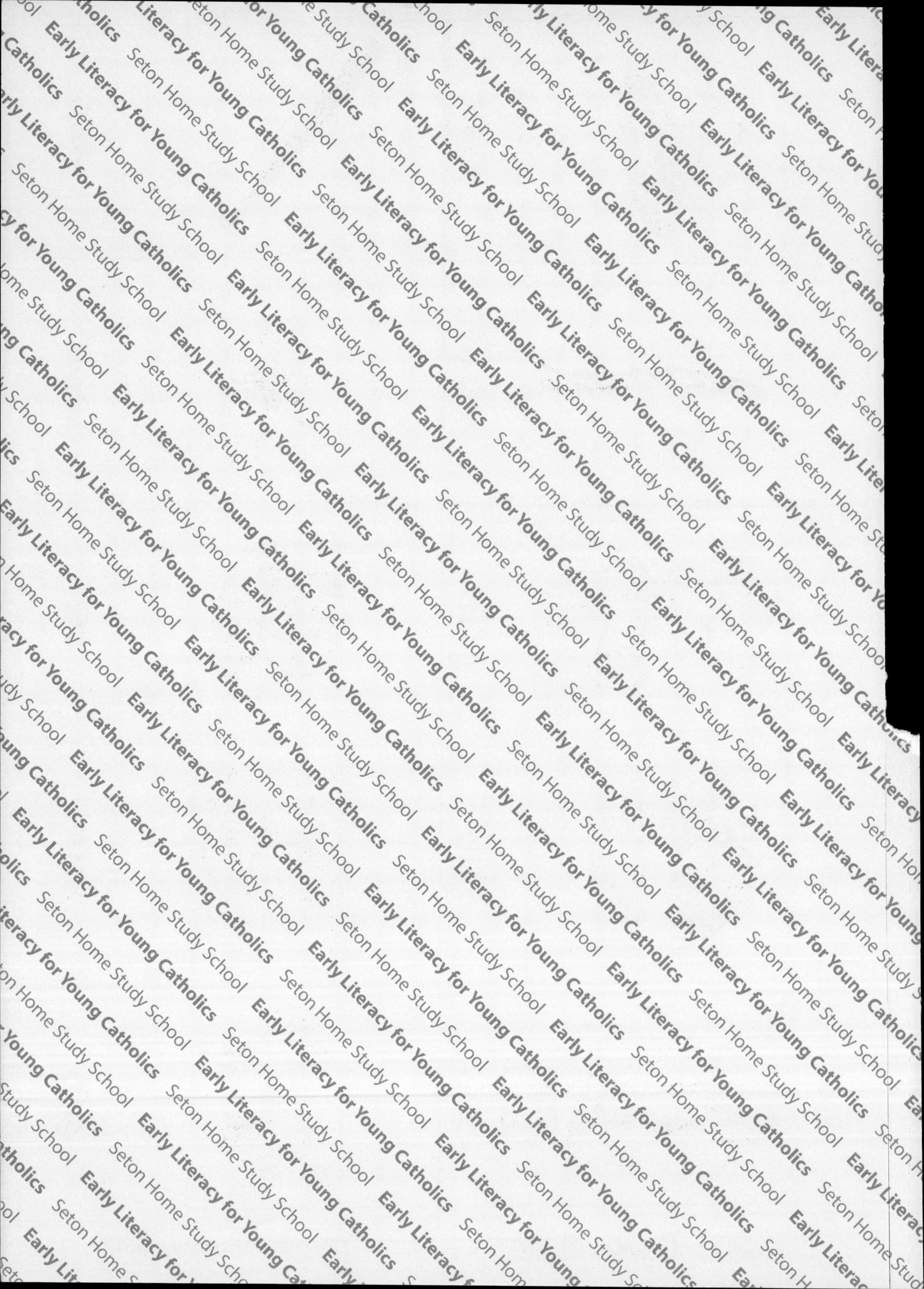

Time to Rhyme: PLAY

Time to Rhyme: DOG

Time to Rhyme: COT

Time to Rhyme: SOCKS

Early Literacy for Young Catholics
Seton Home Study School

Time to Rhyme: DOOR

Time to Rhyme: CAN

Early Literacy for Young Catholics
Seton Home Study School